A PRACTICAL WORKBOOK

STRESS
ANXIETY
DEPRESSION

STRESS ANXIETY DEPRESSION

MARTIN SIMMONS & PETER DAW

WINSLOW

Telford Road • Bicester
Oxon OX6 0TS • UK

First published in 1994 by
Winslow Press Ltd, Telford Road, Bicester, Oxon OX6 0TS
Reprinted 1995, 1997, 1998

Typeset and illustrated by Gecko Ltd, Bicester, Oxon

002-1938/Printed in Great Britain by Information Press Ltd, Eynsham, Oxon

British Library Cataloguing in Publication Data
Simmons, Martin
Practical Workbook: Stress, Anxiety, Depression
I. Title II Daw, Peter
616.85

ISBN 0 86388 122 X

Contents

Martin Simmons is a psychology graduate and qualified social worker with over 10 years' experience in mental health. He has taught psychology, communication skills and mental health at university and college. In addition to this he has worked as management consultant to a wide variety of companies and organizations in the public and private sectors.

Peter Daw is a chartered clinical psychologist with many years of National Health Service experience in his specialist field of adult mental health. A committed eclectic in his theoretical and clinical position, he believes a 'multi-modal model' offers the best approach to the treatment of the wide range of psychological problems presented in his practice. In his Health Service role, he is involved in the planning and development of new therapy services for the public. He provides consultancy and training to Health Service staff.

EDITOR'S NOTE

For the sake of clarity alone, in this text we have used 'he' to refer to the client.

Introduction

This book contains a selection of comprehensive self-help programmes for people who suffer from anxiety, depression and the effects of stress. It is written in the belief that all human beings possess the capacity to influence and change their lives. Moreover, solving personal problems is a skill and like any other skill must be learned and mastered through experience. The exercises and programmes clearly outline the requisite skills and provide a guide for using these skills in organized action plans. The exercises can be freely photocopied to use with your clients. In some cases they will benefit from enlargement on the photocopier.

The book is written in an easy-to-follow style, as free from jargon as possible, so that professional workers from a range of disciplines can use the texts directly with their clients. It is hoped that clients may systematically learn to choose from a variety of coping techniques to meet their individual needs.

In using this book there is no imperative that the user work systematically from Chapter 1 to Chapter 6. Although chapters are sequentially arranged, much of the basic cognitive work in the anxiety management and depression chapters (Chapters 4 and 5), for example, is already covered in Chapters 1–3. Chapter 2, Part 1, on stress, contains information which is relevant to all other topics. The professional workers' knowledge of their clients will enable them to judge which chapters to concentrate on.

Learning requisite skills to cope with life's traumas can have far-reaching benefits:

- achieving confidence in relationships;
- overcoming guilt, anger, moodiness, depression, stress, anxiety;
- communicating easily with others;
- becoming more relaxed;
- solving problems effectively;
- handling conflict and criticism;
- understanding personal choice.

Minds & Bodies

1

This chapter looks at:

- some of the physical reasons why people feel unhappy, anxious or depressed;

- ways of taking simple steps to relax and feel fitter;

- positive steps and helpful techniques to give people control of their own health.

Parts 1 and 2 take a careful look at the basics of life: the air we breathe, the food and fluids we ingest, and how to care for our bodies.

Part 3 concentrates on sleep and introducing relaxation programmes into our daily lives.

Part 4 examines different physical causes of psychological problems and focuses on the use of drugs in treating those problems.

Breathing & Health

Objectives

1 To understand the relationship between physical and mental health.

2 To perfect breathing techniques.

3 To set specific goals for healthier living.

Introduction

This section begins the process of taking more control of our health, the main benefits of which are that a healthy body is more resistant to illness and that positive thoughts and emotions go with a well balanced body. This book seeks gradually to extend this process of control to many other areas of life.

We feel that developing specific strategies for health is the first step towards taking control. Knowing that it is possible to influence what happens in life will provide a solid base from which to approach more complex issues which may lie ahead.

Why health?

With this section barely a page old the writers can hear the protests loud and clear:

"My problems are far too complex to bother about exercising."
"How can breathing make that much difference?"
"My father smoked 60 cigarettes a day all his life and there's not a lot wrong with him."

There are undoubtedly exceptions to every rule, but this should not deter one from aiming towards optimum health.

This book has no wish to preach, merely to inform and guide. There are two important principles here:

1 Having the right information helps us make good choices.
2 Trying to change something in our lives, however simple, shows that we are taking responsibility for ourselves and our future.

Medical research demonstrates a clear relationship between mind and body. If we are suffering from a cold, for example, we find it harder to concentrate and we can often feel emotionally fragile. In other words, our physical health affects our mental and emotional state. Similarly, the process works the other way around. If we are under stress or have had an emotional upset our resistance is lowered and we are more likely to fall ill.

Therefore taking practical measures to preserve and enhance our health will not provide a miracle cure for psychological problems, but *it undoubtedly will help*.

Breathing

Without air we would not be alive. It therefore stands to reason that the way we breathe will directly influence our health and how we feel. This book places considerable emphasis upon correct breathing as an essential life skill if we are to feel good and cope with pressure.

The mechanism for normal healthy breathing is simple. Air is drawn into the lungs and absorbed by the blood, which the heart pumps around the body, including the brain. Therefore, poor air supply results in stagnant blood, which in turn results in an undernourished mind and body.

The brain needs oxygen-rich blood for clear thinking. The digestive system needs healthy blood to use efficiently the food we eat and to expel waste products. Our lungs have a capacity of approximately 5 litres (8 to 9 pints), yet the average breath is but a fraction of this. It follows that deeper breathing increases the efficiency of the lungs and is valuable for overall health and well-being. Unfortunately, the lungs do not move automatically; they are emptied and filled by the surrounding muscles and, like any other muscles, if they are not consciously exercised they become weak and flaccid.

Abdominal breathing exercise

Choose a moment when you feel fairly relaxed and there are no distractions. Sit or lie down comfortably with your back straight, loosening any tight clothing. Place the palms of the hands on your abdomen, middle fingers touching, at a point two to three inches above your navel. Forget about breathing for the moment, but do not hold your breath.

Concentrate upon moving your abdomen gently and rhythmically in and out, so that a small gap appears between the middle fingertips as your abdomen expands and the gap closes again as your abdomen contracts. Count silently to two as you expand your abdomen and again as you move it back. When you have established a gentle and smooth rhythm, notice what is happening to your breathing: if you are taking air in as your abdomen expands and expelling air as it contracts you are practising abdominal breathing!

If it does not happen as easily as that, and for most people it does not, try to start yourself off in the following way. Keeping your hands on your abdomen, as described above, expel all the air from your lungs while contracting your abdomen. Now gently push your abdomen out and allow your lungs to take in air. Now contract your abdomen to expel the air once more, and so on. If you get mixed up, and you find that you get the abdominal movement the wrong way round, stop and start again.

Aim for about a dozen complete breaths per minute (that is, in and out every five seconds). It is important not to hold your breath, so try to make your breathing continuous: as soon as you have breathed in, breathe out, and vice versa. The rhythm is similar to that of the waves upon the sea shore: as a wave reaches its furthest point up the beach so it descends. *If you feel dizzy, you are taking in too much air or breathing too quickly.* Stop for a little while and then start again, trying to breathe more slowly and taking in less air.

Start by practising every day, *only* during quiet, relaxed moments. Relax your shoulders and chest a little more with each outbreath; when you are distracted by a thought or sensation, notice it, let it go and bring your mind back to the movement of your abdomen and the flow of your breath.

We will return to breathing later:

● as an integral part of the health fitness programme;

● in conjunction with stress control and relaxation;

● as a technique in anxiety management;

● to combat tension associated with depression.

We would like to emphasize here that, for breathing techniques to be effective, we need to practise regularly. Only by building regular practice in our daily lives will the benefits be felt. At this stage it would be appropriate for the client to commit himself to a breathing programme, recording *where*, *when* and for *how long* it is intended to practise breathing.

PLACE(S) ....

TIME(S) ....

LENGTH OF SESSION(S) ....

We recommend a minimum practice of twice daily. First practise breathing techniques at home. When a client feels more proficient he can use breathing to boost his confidence in situations that make him tense. Ask the client specifically to identify situations where it would be useful to breathe more effectively, for example in the supermarket or in a business meeting.

1 ....

2 ....

3 ....

4 ....

Emergency Measures

Breathing very rapid, shallow breaths is called *hyperventilation.* There is a feeling of just not being able to get enough air and trying to take bigger and bigger gulps. If this is the case, the blood is being over-oxygenated, causing increased symptoms of anxiety. To overcome the effects of hyperventilation, the following method should be used. Holding a medium-sized paper bag by ringing the open end with the forefinger and thumb, the person should put their mouth to it and breathe into and out of the bag without withdrawing it until the anxiety symptoms have diminished. This works by reducing the oxygen level in the blood and restoring the necessary balance of carbon dioxide. A paper bag should be carried by sufferers at all times in case of need. A more discreet but less effective method is to breathe into cupped hands, trying, as far as possible, to stop the air leaking in between the fingers.

Summary

Breathing is a vital life process. The benefits of breathing properly include:

- enriching the blood supply with oxygen;
- restoring the oxygen/carbon dioxide balance;
- feeling calm and alert;
- learning a skill that will be called upon throughout this book.

Review

Remind clients of the objectives listed at the beginning of this part. Have they fully *understood* and *acted upon* these? If not, return to the relevant section before proceeding.

Diet & Exercise

Objectives

1 To understand the influence of diet upon both physical and mental health.

2 To assess our own fitness.

3 To integrate exercise into our daily lives.

Introduction

The media are saturated with material about health, fitness, diet and so on. Much of its thrust, however, is aimed at slimness, beauty and glamour. This book seeks to enable people to feel better about themselves and their lives, which will involve psychological changes rather than simply losing a few inches around the waist.

People who are stressed or depressed often eat far too much, or starve themselves, or drink excessive amounts of alcohol; this is the *symptom* of the underlying problem and not the *cause*. Treating the symptom will not be sufficient in itself, but will represent a worthwhile step in the right direction.

As with breathing, adopting a healthy diet and exercise regime will not guarantee an end to personal suffering, but it is part of the solution. Taking our health seriously is an important therapeutic step because it indicates that we are taking ourselves seriously. If we are not taking care of our bodies, now is the time to ask *why*.

Diet

We are what we eat. Diet does affect the way we feel. This chapter will help to assess and systematically plan the changes that may need to be made for healthier living.

Diet is for most of us regulated by *habit*. Habits can be a barrier to change. Habits can be self-imposed limits upon our actions.

We must reiterate here that this chapter is not specifically focused on losing weight; it is concerned with healthy living. (For help with eating disorders, see *Useful Names and Addresses*.)

Exercise

The aim of this exercise is for you to educate yourself about diet. To do this you need to research into the body's main sources of nutrients and what constitutes a balanced diet. When you have completed your research fill out the diet-change sheet below.

	Main sources	My main sources	Things I will introduce	Things I will cut down on
Proteins	Meat Fish Nuts Cheese Eggs Beans	Meat Eggs Cheddar cheese	Pulse beans Fish	Red meat Canned meat High fat cheese
Vitamins				
Fibres (non-starch polysaccharides)				
Carbohydrates				

© M Simmons & P Daw, 1994. This exercise may be photocopied for instructional use only.

Sugar

Our diet does not need to include added sugar. Our energy levels are maintained and balanced with other foods: the extra sugar is always only a matter of personal taste.

Hypoglycaemia

Everyone can suffer to a greater or lesser degree from this condition. Hypoglycaemia is usually a mild complaint in which the levels of blood sugar rise and fall quickly with accompanying mood changes. With these rapid fluctuations we may feel fine one moment and anxious, weak and shaky, with a craving for sweet foods, the next.

In more severe cases hypoglycaemia has a wide range of symptoms including migraines, tremors, drowsiness, irritability, poor concentration, fainting, anxiety and depression. The causes of hypoglycaemia include:

- stress,
- sugar,
- smoking and alcohol,
- excess tea and coffee,
- poor diet, irregular meals and erratic slimming plans.

This is how it works:

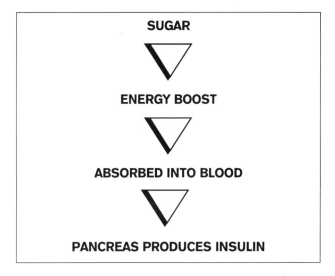

This process repeats itself day after day, year after year until the pancreas becomes super-sensitive and *overreacts* to any sweet food. Thus excess insulin is produced which keeps the body short of sugar/energy, which in turn causes listlessness, nervousness, anxiety and so on. Then more is eaten to produce more sugar, and so the process continues. The culmination is *diabetes mellitus*, when the pancreas becomes worn out and no longer produces any insulin.

This is not the end of the story. In addition to the pancreas taking a daily hammering, the adrenal glands work overtime to help offset the imbalance. Adrenaline (epinephrine), the so-called 'fight or flight' hormone, is released into the body to help the liver release stored glucose, so that we do not need to be continually eating.

Adrenaline has many other effects on the nervous system.

ADRENALINE: 'fight or flight' hormone:
increases the output of blood from the heart with increased heart rate;
increases oxygen consumption and metabolic rate;
releases fatty acids into the bloodstream;
dilates pupils so that more light enters the eyes;
decreases digestion and gut mobility;
constricts gastric and bladder sphincters;
arouses central nervous system.

Adrenaline effectively produces a mini-stress response: that is, the heart beats faster and harder, inducing slight dizziness, nausea and panic. Those who are already prone to feeling anxious and uncertain of themselves are doing themselves no favours by consuming sweet foods. Eating sweet foods:

● causes sharp fluctuations in energy levels and mood;

● overworks the pancreas and adrenal glands;

● mimics the symptoms already shown by those suffering from stress and anxiety.

What to do

Research from the beginning of this part will have revealed which foods are nutritious and which are not.

● cut down slowly on sugar-laden foods such as puddings, cakes, jams, chocolate and sweet drinks.

● Reduce stimulants such as tea, coffee and alcohol. Exclude caffeine drinks before going to bed: there are alternatives.

● Introduce nuts, fruits and vegetables into the diet. These days there are a number of good books which show how to create interesting and appetizing recipes.

● Eat a little and often and try to balance the need for proteins and vitamins. If needing a snack, eat nuts or dried fruit, not sweets.

It will take a few weeks to work on the diet. Positive changes should be made *slowly*; if we slip back now and again, there is no need to worry unduly. Establishing a healthy diet takes time and effort.

A word of caution: working on one's diet is a means to the goal of feeling fitter and healthier. It is important not to become obsessive and rigid about food, as this might introduce a further source of anxiety.

Assess your fitness

Work through the questionnaire below. Write scores in the spaces provided and add up the points at the end.

1 Have you walked a mile at any one time during the last week? *Yes = +1; No = −1.*	
2 Do you avoid physical effort when you reasonably can? *Yes = −1; No = +1.*	
3 Calculate the time over an average week that you have engaged in any exercise sufficient to raise your heart/pulse rate. *Less than 15 mins = −1; 15 mins = +1; 30 mins = +2;* *60 mins = +3; 120 mins = +4.*	
4 Do you avoid foods with high fats and cholesterol such as red meat? *Yes = +2; No = −2.*	
5 Do you eat a high fibre cereal for breakfast? *Yes = +2; No = −2.*	
6 Do you only eat white bread? *Yes = −2; No = +2.*	
7 Do you eat fresh fruit and vegetables most days? *Yes = +2; No = −2.*	
8 How many cups of tea or coffee do you drink each day? *Less than 3 = +2; 3 to 5 = −2; 6 to 10 = −4.*	

	Do you take sugar in your coffee/tea? *Yes = a further –2.*	
9	Do you regularly eat sweet desserts, cakes, sweets? *Yes = –2; No = +2.*	
10	Calculate your alcohol consumption per day. A standard drink is $\frac{1}{2}$ pint of beer or lager, a single measure of spirits, a glass of wine, a small glass of sherry. *0 = +1; 1 to 2 = +2; 3 to 4 = –1; 5 to 6 = –4; 7 to 9 = –10.*	
11	Calculate your cigarette consumption. *Never smoked = +4; ex-smoker = +2; occasional cigar =* *–4; pipe smoker = –6; 1 to 9 = –6; 10 to 20 = –8; above 20 = –12.*	
12	For women who take the contraceptive pill: *Score –4.*	
13	Do you live in a big city? *Yes = –2; No = +2.*	
14	Have you had any viral illnesses in the past year? *None = +2; one = –2; more than one = –4.*	
15	Have you had your blood pressure checked in the past twelve months? *Yes = +1; No = –1.*	
16	Do your gums often bleed when you brush your teeth? *Yes = –2; No = 0.*	
17	For each parent/brother/sister who has had a heart attack before the age of 40: *Score –2.*	
18	For each parent/brother/sister who has been treated for high blood pressure: *Score –2.*	
19	For each parent/brother/sister who had diabetes before the age of 30: *Score –2.*	
20	Do you get headaches or feel unusually weary? *Yes = – 4; No = 0.*	

Scoring

Add up all your scores and record the TOTAL

+15 to + 30 You have not much to learn about fitness.

0 to + 15 Room for improvement.

0 to – 40 Go through the questionnaire and highlight your negative scores. Assess which areas are letting your score down and prepare to make a plan to work on your health. It is time to start taking better care of yourself.

–40 to – 60 Make an urgent appointment with your family doctor and request a medical check-up. Do not put off working on your health any longer.

Before the client commits himself to an action plan he should work through the next section on exercising.

Exercising

It is amazing how easy it is to find excuses for not exercising. We know that there will be benefits to exercising regularly, yet time after time something else comes up to occupy us. Research has shown that regular sustained exercise:

- reduces stress levels,

- helps people feel better about themselves,

- regenerates energy levels.

The scientific rationale behind this is that exercise releases hormones in the brain called *endorphins* which are associated with well-being and relief from stress and pain. In addition to this, feeling good about our bodies and health helps psychological and emotional confidence.

When introducing more exercise into our lives we should follow the following guide lines:

- start slowly;

- do not rush or undertake exercise 'fanatically';

- exercise should be just sufficient to cause sweating and a slight shortage of breath — at this point rest should be taken.

After six to eight weeks of regular exercise the benefit from physical changes in the body will be felt. These include: better circulation, stronger muscles in the heart and around the skeleton, better lung capacity and a feeling of well-being.

What is the problem?

What is stopping us from exercising? Have we started with good intentions and then given up? Can we identify a form of exercise which we enjoy? Are we convinced about the benefits of exercise? Is self-discipline the problem?

The client should make a programme for himself and develop a routine. Remind him not to aim too high to begin with: taking small, simple steps at first is more likely to yield long-term dividends.

One way to help self-discipline is to join a class. Another is to involve family or friends who will offer encouragement and support. The most potent method of sustaining change in our lives is to reward ourselves for our efforts.

Exercise	Day	Time
Swimming	*Mon./Fri.*	*6.00*

Rewards

We are all quick to blame ourselves when we see a fault, but rewarding ourselves gives us an additional incentive to keep trying and proves to ourselves that we are making a special effort.

It is always difficult to initiate and then sustain change, so until we feel the *internal* gain from a new activity we need to identify and use *external* gains. Examples of rewards are a trip out to the theatre/ cinema, a visit to an old friend, a new item of clothing, a luxury gift to oneself.

Action plan

Having worked through the material on exercising and diet we are now ready to make an action plan, in which we list changes we wish to make, identify how and when we will make these changes and decide how to recognize and reward any success.

Diet

Some immediate action I will take is_____

In the longer term I will_____

Exercise

Some immediate action I will take is_____

In the longer term I will_____

Smoking

My plan to reduce/cut smoking is_____

Drinking

My plan to reduce/cut drinking is_____

Rewards

I will use these rewards_____

Summary

- Diet and exercise are vital ingredients to our health.
- Diet directly affects mood.
- Sugar, caffeine and alcohol can cause profound physical and mental problems.
- Exercising enhances health, offsets infection and disease, and helps develop feelings of well-being.

Review

Remind clients of the objectives listed at the beginning of this part.

Have they fully *understood* and *acted upon* these?

If not, return to the relevant section before proceeding.

Sleep & Relaxation

Objectives

1 To learn different techniques for offsetting sleeplessness and to formulate an action plan.

2 To use the total mind and body relaxation routine.

Introduction

Nobody relishes a sleepless night. It is quite normal to wake up in the night, but lying awake and trying to think our way through all of our problems is not a good idea. At night people can feel particularly trapped and vulnerable, so it is important to try to establish healthy sleep patterns. People who experience problems with sleeping will need to consider carefully other areas in their lives where they may experience stress, worry or sadness.

Sleep

- There is no standard time for sleeping; the normal range is from 4 to 10 hours.
- All people sometimes have trouble with sleeping.
- With age we require less sleep but more rest.
- Everyone has to dream, though it is common not to remember your dreams.
- Certain drugs, such as caffeine, certain decongestants, anti-depressants and appetite suppressants are *stimulants* and can ruin sleep.
- Alcohol or sleeping pills can suppress dreaming and cause early waking.

It is, of course, of little comfort to learn that it is 'normal' to sometimes be awake at night when we are tossing and turning in the dark hours. Insomnia is relatively widespread, but for all insomniacs it is the worry about sleeplessness that aggravates the problem. As with many personal problems, worrying and fretting is a very ineffective way to cope — it is better to try systematically to *do what we can* about the problem:

- Establish a bedtime routine: go to bed at a regular time and wind down slowly.
- Avoid stimulants such as coffee and tea from mid-afternoon onwards.
- Avoid catnapping during the day.
- Take exercise each day – physical exertion is conducive to restful sleep — but avoid stressful activity for at least one hour before bedtime. *NB* This does not include satisfying sexual activity which, for many, acts as a soporific.
- Relax, slow down, let go of the day's tensions. Try abdominal breathing (see pages 3–5) as you lie down in bed.
- Stop the inner tape from replaying the day's events or planning the next day's programme. Plan to *block* those thoughts and think of something pleasant.
- Focus the mind on peaceful images. Imagine drifting in a boat on a peaceful lake or being beside a river. Keep returning to the image and coach yourself to *relax*.
- If you cannot sleep, after a specific time (say, half an hour) get up and do something.
- If you must remember something which must be done, have a pen and pad/tape recorder by the bed. Writing it down there and then will lift the burden of consciously needing to remember.

For some people sleep deprivation is a result of a hectic life style. By not listening carefully to our body's needs we ignore tiredness and stay up late even if we need to rise early the next day. Some people work at night and do not allow themselves sufficient time to rest during the day.

Everyone can keep pushing themselves for a limited time, but the long-term consequences of not taking proper care of the body are considerable. (See Chapter 2, Part 1 'Stress'.)

For some people insomnia is only one sign that they have problems in their lives. Treating sleeplessness cannot be the whole answer if there are other issues which need to be addressed. We will return to these in a later section.

Action

I have thought about why I may be having problems with sleeping and I intend to try these remedies:

1 ....

2 ....

3 ....

4 ....

Having decided upon a suitable action plan, try to stick to the new routine for at least two weeks. Habits are not quickly changed and it is unrealistic to assume that problems will disappear with a snap of the fingers.

It is always better to make *modest* promises which can be kept, and then to increase our commitment as we succeed. If we start too ambitiously we may well fall short of our lofty target, lose heart and give up entirely.

Expecting immediate benefits and demanding perfection are two of the most powerful inhibitors to change. It has taken a lifetime to develop our present routines, habits, beliefs, attitudes and responses, so we must:

- allow ourselves time to change slowly;

- allow ourselves to 'fail' sometimes;

- be patient and gentle with ourselves, emphasizing the gains we have made.

Summary

- Everybody needs sufficient sleep.
- The body needs to rest and the brain needs to replenish itself.
- We all need different amounts of sleep and it is important to listen to our body's needs.
- Blocking messages from the body does not make them go away — establishing healthy sleep routines is another way of actively caring for ourselves.

Review

Remind clients of the objectives listed at the beginning of this part. Have they fully *understood* and *acted upon* these? If not, return to the relevant section before proceeding.

Physical Factors & Drugs

Objectives

1 To be aware of physical influences on our health.

2 To understand both the advantages and disadvantages of prescribed medication.

3 To provide a framework for discontinuing reliance on drugs.

Introduction

Stress, anxiety and depression are all accompanied by physical changes in the body. These changes, such as rapid heart beat and nausea, are very real and cannot be disregarded. It is also true that merely treating the *symptom* (such as rapid heart beat) will not work properly if the underlying *cause* (such as fear of supermarkets) is ignored.

This book endeavours to point the way to discovering the various causes of personal distress. There are, however, certain physical influences which directly affect our health.

PHYSICAL ILLNESS WARRANTS A VISIT TO THE FAMILY DOCTOR AS SPECIFIC AILMENTS MAY RESPOND QUICKLY TO MEDICAL TREATMENT.
THIS BOOK DOES NOT CONCERN ITSELF WITH THE EFFECTS OF BIOCHEMICAL FACTORS UPON HEALTH — THESE MUST BE DISCUSSED WITH A PHYSICIAN.

Premenstrual tension

All women are familiar with the changes they feel as they approach menstruation. Symptoms vary from woman to woman, and are of different intensities for different women.

The best way to diagnose effectively how susceptible a person is to PMT is to record accurately any symptoms they have in relation to their menstrual cycle, making a chart with a box for each day in which they can write any symptoms they feel; they can also write in the duration of their menstrual period. After several months they can easily see any relationship between a symptom and their period.

Understanding how PMT may be affecting a woman's moods can help her to avoid unnecessary stresses which she will find harder to cope with. Attending to diet, breathing, exercise and relaxation will also help, as will sharing difficulties with a partner.

There are alternative therapies, such as homoeopathic or herbal therapies, which claim to reduce PMT symptoms.

Viruses and infection

Viral illnesses take a heavy toll upon the body and deplete energy resources. Glandular fever, for example, can leave a person feeling low for months: tired, lethargic, out of sorts, uninterested, and just as they think they are getting better, they fall ill again. This can be particularly taxing in adolescence, when there are so many psychological adjustments to be made.

It is important to take stock of our life style or diet if we are often falling prey to viral illnesses. Physical and emotional stress can increase our vulnerability to infection.

Antibiotics

There is a broad range of antibiotics available, most of which, in addition to their therapeutic effect, can have a depressing influence on one's well-being. Some believe that taking antibiotics depletes our natural immune systems and we can develop a candida infection (thrush) due to the loss of protective benign bacteria. Complementary therapies claim considerable success in alleviating these side-effects.

Other illnesses

Many illnesses and/or the presence of particular hormones can directly influence your mood. Anaemia, diabetes mellitus, hypothyroidism and so on are all diseases which can cause or mimic depression. This book cannot help you diagnose a medical condition: this is a job for the medical practitioner.

Terminal illness

People facing lifelong disabilities, long-term illness or a terminal condition will need to contend with many different feelings. These will include fear, anger, self-pity, depression, blame, denial, envy and loss of confidence.

The reaction to severe illness is similar to that of bereavement. It is normal to suffer an adverse reaction to death or news of cancer, for example. This reaction only becomes pathological when it becomes accompanied by prolonged feelings of guilt, blame and irrational anger. Accepting death or disease or loss of body function always takes time. *Suppressing feelings does not work* — they will reappear and interfere with our daily lives if we try to forget them.

Honestly acknowledging our feelings is a constructive way to greater self-awareness and is stressed throughout this book.

Drugs

Many drugs have a depressant effect on the mind and body. Other drugs have a stimulant effect. The golden rule is make ourselves aware of the effects and side-effects of any drugs we take. By doing this we are assuming responsibility for our own health; with medical advice, we can discontinue drugs which actually make the problem worse. Caffeine, for example, is a stimulant, so it is counter-productive for a nervous sort of person to drink gallons of coffee.

Exercise

Educate yourself about the possible adverse reaction of the following drugs if you take them at all:

- alcohol,
- the contraceptive pill,
- caffeine,
- anti-hypertensives,
- tobacco,
- benzodiazepines (Valium, Lorazepam etc),
- steroids,
- illegal drugs.

© M Simmons & P Daw, 1994. This exercise may be photocopied for instructional use only.

Medication

Most people who have problems with coping are prescribed tranquil-lizers or anti-depressants. Used sensibly, for short periods, they can make a difference and help us through a crisis or bad patch. However, we should not be lulled into a false sense of security: anti-depressants can lift our mood and tranquillizers can mask unpleasant feelings, but there is no pill that can *solve* our problems and conflicts.

For information about medication, talk to the person who prescribed it or send off to MIND, the National Association for Mental Health, for a fact sheet (see *Useful Names and Addresses*).

Coming off medication

Some people have come off their medication by doing no more than vowing never to take their pills again. Most people have much more difficulty than this and would benefit from the following guidelines:

- Consult your family doctor. Share your concern; discuss alternative ways to deal with your symptoms of anxiety and/or depression. *NB* You may feel more confident to tackle this after you have worked through some of the other sections.

- Read again through the literature so that you know what to expect when you reduce or stop the drug. You need to know what any withdrawal effects might be and plan in advance how you intend to combat them.

- Reduce your dosage *slowly*. If you reduce too much too quickly you might find it impossible to cope and give in. Allow yourself setbacks; emphasize your gains.

- Practise alternative coping methods, such as exercise and breathing. Are you practising these skills on a *daily* basis and making them part of your routine?

- If you 'fail', *do not despair*. Try again. Remind yourself of the days when you have survived on a reduced dosage, not the day you slipped up.

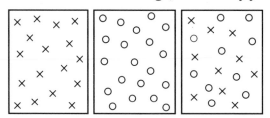

Person A is all good or perfect. Person B is all bad. Person C is a mixture of A and B. Be a Person C: accept your successes and good points; try to get along with your shortcomings. A failure to do this does not make you a failure as a person.

Persons A and B do not exist. It is a mistake to try to become Person A; this only makes the task harder than it needs to be.

Exercise

Plan a work sheet to record steps you will take to reduce reliance on medication. You *may* wish to delay working on this plan until later in the course, though it is recommended that you start today. Drugs merely suppress your symptoms and taking drugs regularly is keeping you in a self-damaging life style rather than demanding you tackle the problem.

Summary

- Our health and moods can be influenced by a number of physical factors such as illness, stimulants or drugs.

- Learning to reduce reliance on drugs goes hand in hand with taking more control of our health. Furthermore, understanding why and when we use drugs will help us pinpoint those areas of our lives that need attention. This is true for both our chosen life style and the way we cope with the demands which such a life style imposes.

- Gradually introducing positive coping strategies such as relaxation and exercise will help promote closer harmony with ourselves and our surroundings.

Review

Remind clients of the objectives listed at the beginning of this part. Have they fully *understood* and *acted upon* these? If not, return to the relevant section before proceeding.

Conclusions

When we are in the right state of mind it is relatively easy to plan for change. For one thing, we have the confidence to believe in the choices we make. For another, we will act upon our decisions.

When personal problems mount up and begin to infiltrate every corner of our lives we lose that confidence and the belief that our actions count for something. We can feel trapped, a victim of circumstance, rather than controlling and directing our lives.

Furthermore, as our minds become increasingly preoccupied with problems, conflicts and worries, so our bodies become unfit and locked with tensions. All of this becomes a vicious circle in which worries and conflicts show themselves in bodily symptoms. These symptoms are then sustained by physical neglect. As the body is neglected so it becomes harder to work through worries and conflicts. It is, of course, very hard to know exactly where to break this vicious circle. One thing is certain, however: worrying about everything and actually doing nothing can only, at the best, keep things the same.

The first chapter has introduced work on some aspects of physical well-being. Breathing, exercising, diet, relaxation and good sleep patterns are all essential ingredients of a healthy life style. Learning to take control of our health is a significant step towards assuming personal responsibility.

Sufficient time must be allowed for the results of small changes in our lives to show. Successes should be rewarded; setbacks should not lead to despondency — it would be asking too much to expect everything to go just according to plan.

By the end of the chapter the client will have learned new skills. He should practise them regularly so that they replace any habits he may have that sustain him in the role of trapped victim.

Achievements

I have worked through the four parts of Chapter 1.	
I have learned breathing techniques and am practising regularly.	
I have taken steps to improve my diet.	
I have introduced exercise into my life style.	
I have reviewed the use of all drugs in my life.	

© M Simmons & P Daw, 1994. This checklist may be photocopied for instructional use only.

If the client is unable to tick any of these statements then he needs to review the material covered in the relevant part of the chapter. Why is he unable to make these changes? Does he understand *why* these things are emphasized?

Working on these areas of his life will undoubtedly help his energy levels. Given time, he will notice the difference and will begin to feel he is relearning to cope.

Life Style

This chapter looks at:

- how stress adversely affects our lives;
- how a systematic problem-solving approach to personal difficulties is an effective method of bringing about change;
- how to choose what we feel, think and do.

Part 1 will increase awareness of stress in our lives. We can assess our stress levels, understand how stress manifests itself and begin to manage stress symptoms effectively.

Part 2 explains how to set realistic goals and achieve them. Businessmen, academics and professionals emphasize careful planning in their work; this book shows how to take systematic steps towards solving personal problems.

Part 3 identifies events in our lives which will influence physical and mental well-being. It also introduces the concept of choice.

Stress

Objectives

1 To understand the relationship between arousal and performance.

2 To check our own stress levels.

3 To monitor how stress manifests itself in our lives.

4 To make an action plan to manage stress.

5 To examine internal causes of stress.

6 To understand the role of thought in creating emotion and stress.

Introduction

Life at the end of the twentieth century is lived at a hectic pace. All of us are having to adapt to a crowded planet of diverse expectations and demands. Stress is some measure of how we cope with the challenge of change.

There are a variety of approaches to managing stress, all of which have their virtues and drawbacks. This book seeks a *balanced* approach, which involves both managing the strains and tensions of today's world and becoming more aware of choices available with regard to self-preservation.

Understanding stress involves understanding ourselves as individuals because no two people respond to any event in exactly the same way. As the client works through the book it is hoped that he will gradually gain greater insight into why he sees things as he does and how, if he so desires, he can change the way he sees things.

One important point to clarify about stress is that we all need *some* stress. It is only when demands on us significantly outweigh our resources to cope that there is a problem. Sometimes these demands are purely material (we cannot afford to replace the car), sometimes they arise from our own attitudes or beliefs (we think we have to be liked by everybody).

Therefore in this chapter the client will need to examine both his circumstances and his inner world. The graph shown below helps to explain why we all need some stress. Along the horizontal axis of the graph is a measurement of arousal. Low arousal signifies lack of interest/apathy. High arousal signifies being overstimulated/'wired up'. Along the vertical axis of the graph is a measurement of level of performance.

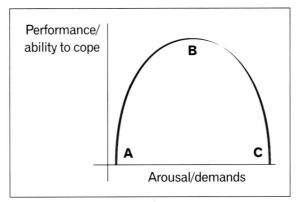

Point A — low arousal gives low performance; that is, we are not sufficiently interested to stir ourselves into action.

Point C — very high arousal also gives low performance; that is, we are too stimulated to act properly: we are 'scared stiff'.

Point B — medium arousal gives the highest performance: we are motivated and firing on all cylinders.

Depressed people lie between points A and B, overstressed people between points B and C.

Check your stress

Read the list of statements below and tick all those which you consider to be true. Assess how you feel generally, though you may wish to place an asterisk beside those statements which you feel are sometimes true.

1	There are not enough hours in the day to get things done.
2	I am usually working to specific deadlines.
3	I never seem to have enough time for things.
4	I become very upset if I am late for an appointment.
5	I find it hard to wait patiently for things.
6	I do everything at once rather than one thing at a time.
7	I usually eat my meals standing up or very quickly.
8	I worry a great deal whether my plans will work out well.
9	I tend to put off important decisions.
10	Once I have made up my mind I stick to it.
11	I cannot name three people who can make me feel good.
12	I do not mix with anyone who introduces me to new ideas.
13	If there is a crisis, it is usually up to me to sort things out.
14	I frequently have less sleep than I feel I need.

15 I tend to hide my feelings from most people.

16 I would describe myself as competitive and ambitious.

17 I do not relax often and take a break from responsibilities.

18 Once I stop work I find it hard to slow down and switch off.

19 I hold back from going to the lavatory when I want to.

20 When things don't go my way I become angry or unhappy.

21 Anger is destructive and should always be restrained.

22 I would like to sleep for a week.

23 I must try and be perfect in all I try to do.

24 When I am working on a particular problem I often get a complete blank and have to stop what I am doing.

25 I find if difficult to say 'no' to people.

26 I find it difficult to complain.

27 I smoke and/or drink and/or eat to excess.

28 I do not sleep well most nights.

29 I have nervous habits like biting my nails/chewing my pen.

30 I am moody.

To score the above questionnaire, count one point for every tick. If you have scored no ticks then you are probably finding it impossible to be honest with yourself. The higher the score, the higher your stress levels. Any score above eight indicates that you will benefit from working through the remainder of this part on stress. You need to reduce your stress levels before they intrude heavily on your life (if they are not doing so already).

© M Simmons & P Daw, 1994. This questionnaire may be photocopied for instructional use only.

More important than any questionnaire, however, is our awareness of the pressures we feel and how we cope with these pressures. Coping with challenge and change is usually healthy up to a point, but it is easy to overdo our commitments. Where do *your* stresses lie:

● at home?

● at work?

● in dealing with people?

Processes

There are three modes in which stress can be experienced: (1) physiological; that is, in our bodies or bodily functions, (2) behavioural; that is, in what we do, (3) emotional/intellectual; that is, in how we feel or think. It is important to understand that these three modes cannot be entirely separated — our minds and our bodies are in constant interrelationship. For example, we will react differently to an event if we are emotionally upset than if we are not.

Physiological

There are two main physiological reactions to stress: (1) the *nervous* pathway, which is the short-term reaction, and (2) the *endocrine* pathway, which is the long-term reaction. The nervous pathway is characterized by the secretion of adrenaline and noradrenaline (norepinephrine). These hormones elicit the 'fight-or-flight' response to a threat in order to help us cope with that threat. The long-term effects of these upon our bodies include:

● restricted mobility, low sex and maternal drives;

● breakdown of protein to glucose, which creates muscle wasting and a reduction of the immune response;

● decreased resistance to infection;

● emotional changes.

The short- and long-term effects of excess stress are considerable and cannot be underestimated. See the table below.

Immediate stress symptoms	Longer-term symptoms
Increased heart rate	Feeling rundown
Increased blood pressure	Backache
Insomnia	Weight loss/gain
Headaches, migraine	Colds, flu etc
Breathing difficulties	Minor ailments
Chest pains	Viral illnesses
Nausea	Heart attacks
Diarrhoea	Ulcers
Vomiting	Colitis
Stomach aches	

Behavioural

There are five main reactions to stress:

1 loss of efficiency — this leads to worry and extra stress;

2 aimless activity to reduce tension, such as drumming one's fingers or picking an argument;

3 focusing on peripheral activities — instead of writing a letter we start cleaning the typewriter;

4 reduced activity, as if we were in physical pain;

5 reduced external stimulation — for example, we withdraw from people rather than seek support.

Check yourself

When stressed I show this behaviour:

	LOW	MED	HIGH
Increased consumption of:			
(a) caffeine			
(b) tobacco			
(c) alcohol			
(d) prescribed medication			
Mood swings			
Aggressive outbursts			
Over/under-eating			
Sleep problems			
Laziness/apathy			

© *M Simmons & P Daw, 1994. This chart may be photocopied for instructional use only.*

Emotional/Intellectual

We have already seen how our performance is affected by our state of mind. If we are either overwrought or uninterested, our performance will suffer. We will become trapped in another vicious circle:

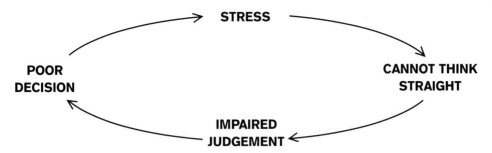

Not only is our thinking impaired, worry precipitates mood changes:

- irritability and flare-ups;
- cynicism, blaming others;
- job dissatisfaction, depression, self-deprecation;
- feeling trapped and isolated.

What are the signs?

Having had the opportunity to assess stress levels and understand how stress manifests itself in our daily lives, it is now time to make an action plan to reduce those stress levels. We are aiming to become sufficiently fit to live our chosen life style.

There are several ways we could suggest of how *not* to continue:

- seek oblivion in drink and drugs,
- take increasing doses of medication,
- isolating ourselves from others and the world,
- be angry and pick quarrels.

> **EXERCISE** Having identified the signs of stress in your life, fill in the charts on page 34. An example is shown to help you do this.

It needs to be repeated that for any of these techniques to be truly effective, they must be practised *regularly*. Lasting benefit will only be achieved if healthy techniques are incorporated into our life style on a regular basis. Having started to make such a terrific effort, the question is how to keep the momentum going. It is particularly difficult to keep 'doing the right things' when problems remain. Remember:

- a journey of a thousand miles begins with a single step;
- if everything is not put right at once, this does not mean it is not worth trying to change *one* thing for the better;
- it has taken a lifetime to become as we are now: it is going to be a struggle to change things;
- keep going, keep going, keep going …

STRESS SYMPTOMS			POSITIVE ACTIONS
PHYSICAL	BEHAVIOURAL	EMOTIONAL	WHAT I CAN DO
Headaches	Less sleep	Irritable	*Relaxation tape*
Nausea	More alcohol	Blaming	*Diet*
Chest pains	More cigarettes	Cynical	*Exercise*
Breathing problems	More benzodiazepines	Forgetful	*Monitor progress*
	Poor diet	Preoccupied	*Set further goals if necessary*

Table 1 *Stress Management Assessment*

POSITIVE ACTIONS	HOW	WHEN	FOR HOW LONG
RELAXATION TAPE	Carry with me	On train Lunchtime	3 weeks

Table 2 *Stress Management Action Plan*

Redefining the stressor

In order to manage our stress effectively we need to do some work with our thinking processes. We all see the world differently; each of us reacts in our own unique way to the world around us. This means that *we* determine what we do or do not see as stressful.

It is possible to reduce stress by looking at the *internal* mechanisms which create and perpetuate feelings of stress. If we suffer from outbursts of rage, mood swings, gloom or self-recriminations, it is appropriate to examine why.

Cognitive psychologists have shown that the way we feel about ourselves and the world depends upon the processes that take place within us before we experience that feeling. If we examine these processes we find that they follow the order of:

1 *perceiving* (see or hearing) an event or situation;

2 *interpreting* the event or situation (to make sense of it to ourselves);

3 *thinking* about the event or situation in a way that is related to our beliefs about how we and the world 'should' be;

4 *feeling* an emotion about the event or situation;

5 *acting* in response to our thoughts and emotions about the event or situation.

All these processes are learned and combined by us as we grow up and build up our own unique body of knowledge about the world from our experiences with parents, siblings, school, friends, work and our own children. It follows that these processes are strongly influenced by what we have experienced in life.

The process of perception is such that what we see depends to a large extent on expectation or SET. An example is the optimist who sees the glass as half-full versus the pessimist who sees the glass as half-empty. It depends on what they expect. We can also actively modify and refine our perception, for example as does someone who decides to become a connoisseur of wine or learn to paint. The concept of SET is explained further on pages 56–57.

The process of interpretation of commonly occurring events takes place extremely quickly. We will not even know that we are doing it. How we interpret an event will depend upon how we have interpreted similar events in the past, but it is also influenced by our present mood and current beliefs about ourselves and the world. In this way the process of interpretation makes our perception more easily palatable to us, but in the process distorts the actual facts.

Following our interpretation of the event or situation that we have perceived we then produce fleeting thoughts about ourselves and our behaviour in relation to our interpretation of the event. If the event is interpreted by us as neutral then we will probably ignore it, producing few thoughts about it. If on the other hand our interpretation of the event indicates that it is important to us in some way, be it positive or negative, then we will automatically produce a number of thoughts about ourselves in relation to the event. The nature of these thoughts depends upon our beliefs about how we and the world 'should' be. For example, if we believe that punctuality is always vital, then any lateness will cause us to produce negative automatic thoughts about the situation.

Following these unbidden thoughts comes the emotion. Whenever we experience an emotion following an event, the cognitive processes of perception, interpretation and thought have automatically and swiftly occurred, sometimes so fast that we have no idea that they have taken place. If the event and the ensuing emotion seem to be of a type that we frequently experience then the cognitive processes in between will become more and more automatic. For instance, following on from the previous example, the negative automatic thoughts create in us the emotion of anxiety if it is we who are late, or anger if it is another.

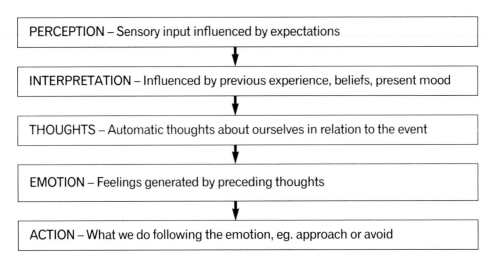

After the emotional response we usually take action. If the event is interpreted by us as neutral then we will not have an emotional response and we may not take any action. If, however, the event is interpreted as important and the ensuing thoughts produce an emotional response then action will result. Behaviour may be appropriate or inappropriate to the facts of the situation, depending on the accuracy of our perception and interpretation of them. Depending upon the nature of the thoughts and emotions we experience, we may feel good about ourselves or bad, we may *approach* the situation or *avoid* it.

> ## Case History
>
> A young man meets a woman at a party. They enjoy each other's company so much that they make arrangements to meet again the following week. However, when they meet for this second time, the man *perceives* that the woman is distracted and inattentive. He *interprets* this perception as meaning that she has lost interest in him. He *thinks*, "She doesn't like me either", in accordance with his belief that he is fundamentally unlovable. He experiences the *emotions* of disappointment and demoralization. He *acts* by making his excuses and leaving.

In this example, errors of perceiving, interpreting and thinking may have led the young man to the wrong conclusion. His perception may have been incorrect — he may just have been focusing upon particular types of behaviour in the woman and ignoring others. His interpretation may have been wrong — she could have been as nervous as he was, or she could be distracted by some event that had occurred that was important to her but about which he knew nothing. His thoughts were automatic and negative and convinced him of a state of affairs for which he had no evidence.

There are three main processes by which thoughts can negatively affect our emotions: (1) illogical or distorted thinking about a situation, (2) too much or too little thinking about a situation, and (3) thinking that stems from underlying irrational beliefs about how we and the world 'should' be. Because all these processes of thinking are automatic and exert a negative effect upon our emotions they are generally called 'negative automatic thoughts'.

Illogical thinking

Cognitive therapists, in particular Aaron Beck, have identified a number of typical 'cognitive distortions' which may result in unpleasant emotion or problems of behaviour.

Emotional reasoning

In emotional reasoning, we reach a conclusion about ourselves or the world based upon an experience of emotion. For example, someone who has an experience of anxiety in a supermarket may tell themselves, "Because I feel terrible in the supermarket, something bad will happen to me there." Other examples of emotional reasoning include: "Because I feel useless, I must be useless", "Because I feel guilty, I must have done something bad."

To counter this tendency we need to remember that *feelings are not facts*.

Overgeneralization

Overgeneralization refers to extreme cases of reasoning from the particular to the general. Put another way, we overgeneralize if we draw a general and unwarranted conclusion from a single piece of evidence. We are warned against this in the saying 'one swallow does not make a summer'. If we take the example above of the young man who thought he was rejected on his date, he would have overgeneralized if he had concluded, "I always get rejected."

To counter this tendency we need to remember to *examine the evidence*.

All-or-nothing thinking

All-or-nothing thinking means seeing things as either black or white but never as a shade of grey. Thinking in this way will convince us that we have failed completely if we have not attained perfection. Perfectionism (see below) is thus a form of all-or-nothing thinking. But all-or-nothing thinking is not confined to the way we think about ourselves. How many times have we said to someone close to us, "You always ..." or "You never ..."?

All-or-nothing thinking can cause anxiety in us when it is focused on our own behaviour. Equally, it can cause anger and resentment when it is focused on someone else's. To counter this tendency we need to learn to use *relative terms*, such as 'often' and 'frequently', rather than 'always', 'rarely' and 'occasionally' instead of 'never'.

Magnifying and minimizing

This refers to the tendency to overemphasize or underemphasize the meaning of an event. When we experience negative emotion as a result of this cognitive distortion it is usually because we have magnified our weak points and/or minimized our strengths. An example is the efficient but pressurized businessman who misplaces a paper and then thinks, "I am so disorganized." Another is the anxious athlete who achieves a personal best before the championships but thinks, "I did all right there, but it will not make any difference to how I perform on the day."

Again, the way to counter this tendency is to *examine the evidence* for the interpretation. When little or no evidence is found for the conclusion then its impact is weakened.

Selective negative focus

This describes the way we focus on the negative aspects of a situation and ignore the positive ones. This universal tendency is reflected in our adoption of 'Murphy's Law' which apparently states, 'If anything can go wrong, it will'. When considering routine activities we tend only to remember those occasions when something different happens, and in routine activities when something different happens it usually means something going wrong. We do not remember the countless times that everything went smoothly. However, selective negative focus refers to a more extreme version of this tendency — by dwelling *only* on the negative details we conclude that the whole situation is negative. For example, there is the grade A student who, following an important exam, focuses only on the questions that she believes she answered wrongly and concludes that she has failed.

This tendency is closely associated with irrational beliefs about perfectionism (see below).

Arbitrary inference

This involves making unjustified connections between perceptions or ideas which are not related at all, or which are related in a very different way, and then jumping to a negative conclusion. You will remember in our first example of the young man on a date that he interprets his companion's inattentiveness as being evidence that she has lost interest in him. He thought, "She is ignoring me, that means that she doesn't like me any more." While this is one possible hypothesis, it hardly amounts to a logical conclusion. This example demonstrates a particular kind of arbitrary inference called *personalization* which occurs when we interpret a situation as meaning something negative about ourselves, regardless of the evidence, or lack of it.

Other types of arbitrary inference are mind reading and predicting the future. In the first of these, we draw conclusions about what others think about us, often basing these conclusions on negative opinions that we hold about ourselves, such as "He thinks I am incompetent because I sent that report late" or "She will not want to invite me to her party now that I have let her down over the babysitting."

To counter this tendency we need to *examine the evidence* and, where it is lacking and the need to know persists, *gather evidence.*

Predicting the future, also called 'fortune-telling', is a self-explanatory term describing thoughts which influence our attitude towards future events. The conclusions drawn are arbitrary and may involve a process of overgeneralization, as described above. An example is the learner-driver who makes a mistake during his first lesson and predicts, "I'll never learn to drive."

To counter this tendency we need to *examine the evidence.* We often want to have an idea of what the future holds and to do this properly we need to gather evidence. In the above example, this might mean the learner-driver asking his instructor how many first-timers make that kind of mistake, how many lessons people usually need before they stop making that kind of mistake, and so on.

Exercise

Use the chart below to record your own examples of cognitive distortions, with the situations in which they occur.

SITUATION	THOUGHT	COGNITIVE DISTORTION
My son forgets my birthday	He does not love me	Magnifying

Too much or too little thinking

The kind of thinking that causes negative emotion may not necessarily be illogical; it may seem accurate, logical and realistic. However, it may still have the effect of producing negative emotion and impeding our actions. Two specific types of this kind of thinking are the following.

Rumination

This describes a process of too much thinking — repetitive, unproductive thinking in which we run over a thought, whether logical or illogical, again and again.

Thought avoidance

This describes a process of too little thinking, wherein we avoid thinking about a problem that really needs our attention.

Often rumination and thought avoidance operate in tandem. We may concentrate and ruminate about the less significant or unchangeable features of a problem while avoiding thinking about the parts of the problem that really affect us or that we can really change.

Irrational beliefs

We all maintain a framework of beliefs about ourselves and the world to which we refer constantly to make sense of our experience. Because these beliefs are developed in a rudimentary way very early on in our lives they may not be subject to the reason and rationality which we imagine characterizes our adult thinking. Indeed, all of us maintain some beliefs that can only be described as irrational. These beliefs influence our thoughts, which in turn influence our emotions and behaviour (see also pages 60–62).

Perfectionism

For all of us there are times when we seek perfection and feel useless if we fall short of the mark. If we seek perfection in many areas of our life this results in things taking so long other tasks are left undone, an increased volume of things to do and always feeling short of time.

It is important to recognize that *nobody* actually ever achieves perfection. With ever-higher standards and a lack of time there comes a loss of self-esteem, self-blaming, and increased frustration and irritability. An example of perfectionism is keeping the kitchen floor spotless. We could all confess to others. The consequences of maintaining perfectionism include the following:

1 We think that perfect solutions *are* possible.

2 We blame ourselves or others ("If it were not for … I would feel better.")

3 We procrastinate: important tasks are put off for fear of failure.

4 We impose our standards on others and become difficult to live with.

Rigidity

There are certain aspects of us all which are relatively inflexible. People who are fixed in their ways demand that things be done in a fixed and specific way, insist that certain procedures must be adhered to and claim there is only one way of doing things. Any deviation from this causes a sudden eruption of irritability, frustration or anger.

Equally important is rigidity of opinion. Rigid opinions have their origins in fixed values and attitudes. We can all think of people who are inflexible and how they make us feel. Are there areas of our lives that are fixed? How can we reduce these?

Absolute thinking

This refers to the notion that we hold absolute rules for the way we and others behave rather than relative guidelines which allow flexibility. If those rules are broken we feel great turmoil. Absolute words include never/always/must/should, as in 'I must always …', 'People must treat me …' and 'I must be listened to or …'. We can all think of our own examples of absolute thinking.

Catastrophizing

One of the most common fantasies we play in our heads is what would happen if we failed at something. We catastrophize when we imagine failure with such words as awful or terrible. Would it really be awful if we failed at something?

Consider the example of a businessman who works hard to complete a report which the boss does not even read. The businessman is upset, rude to everyone, goes home and takes it out on his family. In this example our businessman holds the irrational belief that he must always be acknowledged for his good work and if he is not then that is terrible (that is, a catastrophe).

A second example is the secretary who misfiles a document and, when attention is drawn to this, becomes moody and depressed. In this example the secretary holds the irrational belief that she must never make mistakes because, if she does, that implies she is worthless. We can all think of our own examples when we catastrophize and thus hold irrational beliefs about ourselves.

It should be noted, finally, that we all have a combination of the above processes operating. Later on we will return to this topic to work on changing thought processes. At this stage it is sufficient to be aware of these processes. We *all* use these perceptual and thinking patterns as a way of seeking stability and security in the world. We *all* try to impose certain values and standards to make our world an understandable and controllable place to live in. Stress occurs when we perceive a transgression of these standards or when we apply distorted thinking processes in an attempt to deal with situations. We have seen that, when these beliefs are too rigidly held or the thought processes associated with them are illogical, the very *solution* we have applied to deal with the insecurity of our lives becomes the cause of greater insecurity. If standards are set impossibly high, stress levels rise further.

Summary

In this part we have assessed stress levels, learned how stress manifests itself, made an action plan to reduce external sources of stress and considered in detail the thought processes that create internal sources of stress. Reducing the need to control life tightly is a crucial step towards taking a more relaxed attitude to life. This will significantly reduce our feelings of stress.

Review

Remind clients of the objectives listed at the beginning of this part. Have they fully *understood* and *acted upon* these? If not, return to the relevant section before proceeding.

Setting Goals

Objectives

1 To grasp the importance of a systematic approach to personal change.

2 To learn how to set long- and short-term goals.

3 To set a personal long-term goal.

Introduction

Most people rarely solve their personal problems in an orderly manner. If they have a legal problem they see a solicitor; a crack in the ceiling warrants a visit from the surveyor. Personal and interpersonal problems, however, are put aside, suppressed and, at best, muddled through in a haphazard 'tomorrow is another day' way. It is hardly surprising that things do not change — other than deteriorating perhaps.

One reason why personal problems are not systematically dealt with is that they are painful and unpleasant. It is because they are painful and unpleasant that we have elected to work through them. Another reason for assigning personal problems to the 'pending' tray is that we are never taught how to cope with emotional difficulties. We can join a course on hanging wallpaper, on mending a car or growing a weed-free lawn, but there is nothing on dealing with anxiety, stress, depression, anger and so on.

Setting goals is a crucially important skill — planning properly greatly enhances the chances of solving problems.

Long-term goals

We all make plans for our future. For example:

- I hope to travel.
- I would love to throw a party everyone would remember.
- One day I am going to write a novel.

Sometimes these goals are vague:

- I want to be spiritually fulfilled.
- I want to be more creative.

Other goals are specific:

- I want to be promoted.
- I want a part-time job.

In order to make *meaningful goals* we need to state clearly (1) what we want, (2) how we are going to get it, and (3) how long it is going to take us. These three factors are *definite*, *objective* and *visible*. A clear goal should have all these three facets. Consider, for example, "I am going to learn how to drive." This says *what* we want, but nothing about *how* we intend to learn, what *time scale* is involved or even *how we will know* when we have got there.

The goal should read:

Goal: I am going to learn to drive so that I can pass my driving test.
How: I am going to book weekly driving lessons with 'Drivewell'. I am going to practise with my wife every Wednesday and Saturday tea-time.
Time: I am going to take my test six months from now.

Compare the above with these goals:

- I want to be less anxious.
- I want to do more.
- I want to be more confident at parties.

If we consider the first of these we can make a clear goal:

1 How will you know whether you are less anxious?
2 What criteria will you use to measure your anxiety?
3 What situations are the most important for you to remain calm in?

Revising the goal we have:
Goal: I want to travel by subway or underground without taking Valium or hyperventilating or becoming sick.

Now we know *exactly* what you want, we can plan how we will achieve the goals.
How: I will practise breathing exercises … times a day. I will purchase a 'personal stereo' on which I can play my relaxation tape when I am outside the house. I will start by taking three trips of one stop with my best friend.

Now we have planned our method, we should put a time on the exercise. Without this we could be working on this for the next 20 years.

Time: Commence abdominal breathing today. Purchase the 'personal stereo' this Saturday. Take my first trip two weeks from today. Travel on my own for at least six stops one month from today.

This may sound too concerned with detail. It cannot, however, be said too often that working on personal problems is *never easy*. There are a thousand distractions and excuses we can find to put off the day when we start trying to take control. Setting proper goals is good self-discipline. If change did not require self-discipline, we would have easily worked out things by now. Systematic method in anxiety management is covered in more detail in Chapter 4.

Exercise

Write below three long-term goals for yourself (these goals can be anything you wish):

1	....
2	....
3	....

Now split the goal which you think has the greatest priority for you into:

Goal	....
How	....
Time	....

Have you written things which are definite, objective, visible?
If you have used worlds like *happy, depressed, better at, next year,* cross them out and start again. Be specific.

Getting help

It is appropriate to enlist the help of others. We may find that we can use others to encourage us, or remind us, or even to share in our triumphs.

Feedback from others is important but, as adults dealing with our own lives, we should remember: we dictate the speed of things, we set our own standards, and it is OK to get help with things. There is *no such thing as failure* here. Mistakes are for learning more about ourselves: Why am I not reaching this goal? What is standing in my way? How can I proceed now? How far have I come already? We need to list our achievements and our strengths. How much further do I need to go? Am I being realistic? Am I trying to be too perfect? (See pages 41–42).

It is better to succeed at a simple goal than to fail at a bigger one.

Overcoming negative thoughts

We all hold ourselves back and sabotage our attempts to change with negative thoughts. A negative vocabulary uses words like: impossible, can't, yes, but, ought to, should, if only …. Commonly used evaluations are: dreadful, awful, terrible.

Some things, such as the loss of a loved one, the loss of a limb or the house burning down, are awful. Other things we may call awful, but they are not really. Is it awful that the car breaks down or the supermarket is always busy? It is inconvenient, but not on a par with losing a limb. Telling ourselves over and over that things are awful generates strong emotions and they will prevent us from getting started.

Exercise

Make a list of negative words which you find yourself speaking or thinking. Try to find ways of changing these words. For example, instead of "It is impossible for me to hang wallpaper" it is preferable to say: "I am not brilliant at decorating, but *I will try* to hang the wallpaper."

The change is subtle but it gives you some breathing space, stops you filling yourself with negative thoughts and feelings, and allows you to concentrate on the effort you are making, rather than simply on the task itself.

Another example: "I am the sort of person who always messes things up" may be restated as: "I may not be perfect, but I am going to have a go."

Working on thoughts is a key component of this book and will be returned to in Chapters 3, 4 and 5.

Short-term goals

Many long-term goals need to be broken down into steps. Some problems are overwhelming in their magnitude and complexity and as a result never get started. A commonly used analogy is climbing Mount Everest. If we wish to climb Mount Everest then this is a long-term goal. In the shorter term we must become fit, purchase equipment, practise on smaller mountains, and so on.

It is therefore a good idea to break down the daunting long-term goal into smaller, manageable chunks. Thus, rather than becoming overwhelmed by a goal of 'landscaping the garden', we could break it down into:

- consulting an expert,
- drawing a plan,
- planting the lawn,
- building the rockery.

If this is still too complex it can be broken down further. Thus building the rockery becomes:

- collecting stones,
- buying compost,
- selecting the plants,
- planting specimens,
- feedback from the expert.

Each of the above can then be split into

Goal	....
How	....
Time	....

This enables us to be systematic and also prevents our putting unrealistic demands upon ourselves.

If we do split a larger goal into smaller steps then it is important consciously to remind ourselves what we are doing and why we are doing it. It is common to give up a task if we can no longer see the relevance to the greater goal.

Exercise

Return to the goal you set yourself on page 46. Do you need to split this goal into smaller steps?

My long-term goal is ....

My short-term goals are (fill in the table below):

GOAL	HOW	TIME

Summary

Counsellors and psychologists use goal setting as an integral part of their professional practice. In order for the goals to be effective they need to clearly identify what, how and by when. When we have identified a goal for ourselves we may need to split it into smaller steps.

Review

Remind clients of the objectives listed at the beginning of this part. Have they fully *understood* and *acted upon* these? If not, return to the relevant section before proceeding.

Life Events & Choice

Objectives

1 To highlight major events in our lives which can affect our well-being.

2 To highlight major sources of personal unhappiness.

3 To understand how choices influence decision making.

4 To identify thinking processes that undermine the making of choices.

Introduction

This part will highlight some of the factors in our lives which may be exerting a negative influence. It is impossible to make a definitive list of factors because, as we have seen, different people react differently to events. As a rule of thumb, however, if we believe something is stressful, then it will be.

Life periodically throws up 'major events' and, if we do not properly acknowledge our feelings about these events, they are buried away and can exert a hidden influence. Hiding what we think are unacceptable feelings is a passport to depression.

There are some situations in which it is normal to feel unsure of ourselves, unhappy, angry and so on. There is a problem if we cannot identify and then let go of those feelings and we turn them either against ourselves or against those close to us.

Major life events

Childbirth

- Physical stress on the mother, including upset of hormonal balances.
- Emotional stress on the mother:
  change of body image while pregnant;
  disruption of routines with partner (for example, tiredness, lack of sex);
  feelings of being a poor mother.
- Emotional stress on the father:
  change of routine, being less looked after;
  feelings of resentment, jealousy, anger.

Death

Grieving is a process which can take us through emotions ranging from despair, to self-blaming, to anger. (See also pages 22–23.) If our feelings become 'stuck' and cannot be adequately expressed we may develop nervous and/or depressive symptoms.

Family life

- Marriage.
- Marital quarrels.
- Introduction of children into the home (also stepchildren).
- Adolescence.
- Children leaving home.
- Separation and divorce.

All of the above take their toll upon us. It is normal to experience a wide range of emotions within a family. It is very abnormal never to express them to one another. Communication in families is an exceedingly complex process, and poor communication is a major source of family discord or break-up.

Work

- Ambition.
- Demotion or becoming stuck.
- Redundancy or unemployment.
- Conflict at work, such as racism, sexism.

In Western culture men in particular define themselves in terms of work. Unhappiness or stress at work is quickly transferred to the home and family. Similarly, unhappiness at home is introduced into work and results in a lowering of efficiency.

Women who define themselves only in terms of being a housewife can find this very inhibiting. Furthermore, the 'super-woman syndrome' of working/managing the home/caring for the family sets unrealistically high standards.

Moving house

Moving house has been shown to be one of the chief sources of stress. How well we cope with change is a useful indicator of our mental and emotional health. For people who emigrate the problem can become very severe if anyone in the household feels isolated and lonely.

Family holidays

Two weeks of supposed relaxation all too often turn out to be exactly the opposite. A foreign holiday may involve a difficult journey, adjustments to the climate and food, disruption to normal family relationships and much more. Even the planning of a holiday can bring couples to grief.

Emotional events

Our present emotional potential may either be enhanced or denied depending on how we have reacted to life events. How we are now is in all likelihood somehow linked to our past — this is not to imply a simple cause and effect relationship between our past and our present; nor is it an opportunity to blame our past. It is more likely that a catalogue of events or circumstances have influenced our present emotional make-up. The sort of events which create bottled up emotions are:

- Physical or sexual abuse.
- Divorce of parents.
- Early hospitalization.
- Death of parent(s).
- Changing schools.
- Bullying or excessive criticism or punishment.

If we feel that past events are exerting an excessive negative influence on our present, professional help should be sought.

Major sources of unhappiness

Coping with things that happen in life is one thing, but many people have to cope with a life where things are *not* happening. Some people are not getting married, cannot move house or cannot go on holiday.

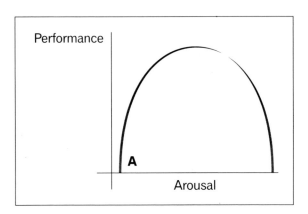

People at point A have insufficient stimulation to perform at a satisfying level. When things become monotonous and we feel that we are only marking time, it is a short step to a sense of futility and depression. (See page 29 for further explanation of this graph.)

Loneliness

Some people cultivate lives for themselves in which they are as detached and independent from other people as is possible. For others this is not their wish, it is imposed on them. Loneliness has a massive influence on unhappiness. It can make some withdrawn and passive, and can lead others to go on an uncontrolled and unfulfilling pursuit of social contact. Loneliness is within us all and needs careful management for those who have less opportunity to commune with others.

Boredom and underachievement

Boredom at home or at work is also difficult to contend with. Typically, women who do little other than housework and child minding fall victim to stagnant routines. These are often difficult to challenge because people feel trapped by others' expectations of them. Commonly, feelings of dissatisfaction are repressed as 'unworthy of a good mother'. This, of course, fails to recognize that *quality*, not quantity, of mothering is what matters most.

Unemployed men can often feel effectively 'castrated' and, in an effort to seek dominance or simply a recognized role in the household, end up in conflict with their partners.

Dissatisfaction is usually the precursor to change. But boredom at work can often lead to frustration and feelings of defeatism: "After all, there is the mortgage, the kids, the summer holiday..." Just as a woman can feel trapped at home, a man can feel trapped at his workplace. Denying our feelings and neglecting our creativity are recipes for dissatisfaction and, if not dealt with, depression.

Freedom and necessity

There are constraints upon us that we cannot change. There is little point being upset about the colour of our eyes, for example. The majority of our lives fall into two categories:

FREEDOM	NECESSITY
Choice	No choice
I will	I should
I want	I ought

Deciding about issues in the freedom column is relatively easy: what course to do at university, what car to drive, what clothes to wear. The necessity column is where the difficulty arises.

First the necessity column is subdivided thus:

Mandatory	Arbitrary
Colour of eyes, ethnic origin, etc	Whether a woman should also work outside the home etc.

Some aspects of our lives are mandatory and therefore pose little or no conflict. It is in those areas where we perceive constraint that conflict arises. Conflict arises because we see forces opposing our wishes. These are called arbitrary constraints because, unlike eye colour, they involve personal choice.

When arbitrary constraints are seen as external forces we feel stuck. Thus it seems as if a decision whether to work or not is as controlled as the colour of our eyes. How does this process work? In the example of the woman wanting to work outside the home, she is held back by three factors: (1) "I must look after my children", (2) "I must run the home" and (3) "My husband will not like me working."

The loyal housewife/mother feels constrained by these three factors, which are seen as external. Thus children, home and husband are preventing her from working. She says to herself, "I have no choice." If we repeat to ourselves enough times: "Yes but", "If only" and "I have no choice", the last statement will be true.

In this example, other external factors also exist, such as "I'll find a child minder", "Other families manage with working parents", "I'll talk to my husband about it" and "I'll find a way somehow", but these are forgotten and 'There is no choice' seems to reflect how it feels. Some people reduce all conflict in their lives by running them according to necessity:

the less issues there are to consider, the less there is to worry about. But when there is *nothing* to worry about, when we have relieved *all* the conflict — and stay at home with the children, cleaning and cooking meals, even at the weekends — we also lose responsibility for making decisions. When we lose responsibility we lose authority and significance. The descent into hopelessness becomes inevitable.

We all live with both freedom and necessity. When we confuse freedom with necessity and we say "I cannot" (because of external factors), we mean "I will not" (because we are unwilling to face up to things or make a decision). If we feel unable to choose for ourselves we need to ask ourselves *why*.

Case History

Malcolm's mother left home when he was five years old, leaving him with his father and two-year-old sister. As Malcolm grew up he realized he was angry at his mother. He didn't always treat her considerately. In his relationships with women he always backed off before they came too close.

"That's the way I am", he would say. He felt that he was fixed by his past. His mother leaving him was a fact — no amount of therapy could change that. He felt constrained by necessity: he felt bad because his mother had left home. In time he realized that, even though his mother's deserting the house was an indisputable fact, how he felt about this was not. He had the freedom to forgive her, to understand why she left. He had the freedom to feel differently: he was only bound to the event if he chose to be. He also had the freedom to bear a grudge, be angry, hurt, fearful.

Eventually he understood that he had sacrificed his freedom for necessity. He blamed his mother for all his bad feeling, when the feeling was his own to choose. (In some ways it was comforting to be a victim and rewarding when people felt sorry for him.)

Forgiving her was like relieving himself of an oppressive burden.

Understanding our choices gives our lives a degree of control, relieves us from being dominated by the past and lessens the fear of the future.

Choosing

We now consider our capacity to make choices and decisions as a child:

● Were we consulted about family holidays?

- Were family issues discussed with us?
- Did our parents intrude upon our choices of clothes or friends?
- Do we feel constrained by the 'family way' of doing things?
- Were we encouraged to think things out for ourselves?

If we were constrained from making choices as a child then we may have corners of our minds filled with anger, frustration and resentment. If not dealt with, these feelings might be projected onto others areas of our adult life, such as our work and our family. Becoming aware of this process is a significant step towards freeing ourselves from the bondage to pain stored in the past.

"This always happens to me!"

How often have we said this to ourselves? Does history repeat itself? Does life seem to be going round in circles?

Psychologists use a concept called SET to help explain how we come to see both objects and events in a fixed way. A simple example is the SET for a chair — four legs, a back, a seat — which we gradually learn from infancy through childhood. Thus SET describes the frameworks that we construct to represent objects for ourselves, but it also applies to *events*. For example, we plug in the electric kettle and expect the water to boil. On occasions the water does not boil and then we usually feel surprised. There may be good reason for the water not boiling — a power cut, a burnt-out element or blown fuse and so on — but we feel resentful when our expectations are not fulfilled.

This is much more the case when *other people* do not behave according to our expectations. We all seek stability in our relationships, but problems occur when our need to predict the outcomes of actions and events is overdeveloped. Thus, if our SET for another person is not fulfilled, we feel confused and even angry. SET, therefore, is a fixed way of perceiving and also applies to the way we understand ourselves.

What happens when we have an external SET, as expressed by, for example, "Whenever I try a DIY job it goes wrong", or "Whenever I try to please my partner, I am misunderstood"? Here the implication is that the consequences of our actions are both inevitable and beyond our control. If we think we *always* have bad experiences in *every* situation we begin to feel we have no choices. Having no choices, as we have seen, is a passport to gloom and despondency.

Thus assuming our actions, feelings and thoughts are externally controlled maintains us in the role of powerless victim. To challenge and change our SET, we need to ask ourselves key questions:

1 Does ... *always* happen that way, or only sometimes?

2 Does ... occur in *every* situation, or only on some occasions?

3 Does ... *never* occur, or only rarely?

4 Is ... *totally* beyond our control, or are there things we could do about it?

5 *Must* we feel/think about ... in a fixed way?

In the example of 'always being misunderstood', is this always the case or are there times when we are not misunderstood? Does misunderstanding occur at other times, such as when we are not trying to please our partner? What about our methods and timing in attempting to please our partner?

"But that's the way I am" is another commonly used plea to excuse personal responsibility. The expression implies that we cannot change, that it is beyond our capability to change. The principle of this book is, on the other hand, that we could all change, providing we are prepared to analyse objectively how we think, feel and act, and then take steps towards assuming personal responsibility for the way we prefer to be.

Summary

We are all engrossed in the pattern of our lives. Sometimes we feel trapped, oppressed, controlled. Feelings that are beyond our control create frustration and, at times, hopelessness.

There are some situations in which it is normal to feel unsure of ourselves, unhappy, angry and so on. There is a problem if we cannot identify and then let go of those feelings and we turn them either against ourselves or against those close to us.

Comprehending the choice behind our feelings can liberate us from their chains. Understanding ourselves more fully will help us make choices based on "I'm all right" rather than negative evaluations such as "I'm to blame for this."

Review

Remind the clients of the objectives listed at the beginning of this part. Have they fully *understood* and *acted upon* these? If not, return to the relevant section before proceeding.

Conclusions

In this chapter we have taken a closer look at the way we are leading our lives. If we are caught up in a life style which is either too demanding or too understimulating we can experience psychological problems such as anxiety, loss of confidence, low self-esteem and depression. If this is the case, there are several questions we need to ask ourselves:

- What methods can I employ to manage the stress in my life more effectively?
- If I identify changes I need to make, how can I systematically plan for these changes?
- What choices am I making about my life style?

This chapter has, we hope, helped to answer the above questions. There are not, of course any simple answers. The authors cannot dictate any hard and fast rules: it is up to the individual to learn how to assess problems and possible methods which can be employed to help work towards solutions.

Achievements

I have worked through the three parts of Chapter 2.	
I have learned how stress manifests itself in my life.	
I have taken steps to manage my stress levels.	
I have used goal setting as a problem-solving method.	
I have looked at the choices I am making in my life.	

© M Simmons & P Daw, 1994. This checklist may be photocopied for instructional use only.

If the client is unable to tick any of these statements then he needs to review the material covered in the relevant part of the chapter. Why is he unable to tick the boxes? Does he understand *why* these things are emphasized?

Having started the process of objectively analysing his life and how he thinks, *he* can proceed to Chapter 3.

Understanding Ourselves

This chapter looks at:

- the way psychologists classify our experience, and thus gauge an effective treatment method;
- a method to analyse carefully our own experience;
- effective and ineffective ways of coping;
- the way we defend ourselves against feelings, and their consequences on our relationships.

Part 1 distinguishes between action, feeling and thought as distinctive components of experience.

Part 2 provides a model for assessing ourselves and asks us to observe ourselves closely.

Part 3 examines the ways used to cope with difficulties. It will help us to orientate ourselves towards effective ways of dealing with things.

Part 4 orientates us towards key dynamic psychological concepts.

Basic Psychology

Introduction

There are three basic principles which may be applied throughout this book:

1 The principle that it is possible for each of us to influence our own behaviour.
2 The principle that influencing or changing our behaviour is a skill. Like any skill, it must be gradually mastered and learned from experience.
3 The principle that formulating a definite action plan is the most effective method of systematically working through problems.

This chapter aims to help everyone understand their own psychology. By this we mean very specifically:

● Our behaviour: our actions, what we do.
● Our emotions: how we feel.
● Our thoughts: how and what we think.

When everything is running smoothly these three parts of our total psychology work together in harmony. We are happy when what we think and what we feel and what we do are consistent with each other. We have problems when what we think and what we feel, for example, are at odds with each other: "I think it is good to work but I feel very claustrophobic and panicky in interviews." Here the thoughts and feelings are pulling in different directions. In this example the person avoids going for an interview (not going for an interview is a behaviour). As a result of this the person feels depressed because their life is being disrupted by their personal problems.

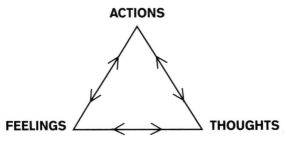

Actions, feelings and thoughts, then, are constantly in relationship with each other. It is important to learn how to distinguish between them because different types of therapy concentrate on different areas. Any person who wishes to change their life will need to be objective and to distinguish clearly between what they do, feel and think.

Actions

- When I feel myself getting depressed *I take anti-depressants*.
- Because I was isolated *I joined an evening class*.
- When he came home drunk *I threw his dinner at him*.
- When she telephoned *I burst into tears*.
- *I had a stiff drink* when I heard the house sale had fallen through.

The italicized statements refer to clearly *observable* actions.

Feelings

- I have just spring cleaned the house and *I feel great*.
- I walked out of my office and *I feel stupid now*.
- *I have been very worried* about not hearing from my mother.
- *I get so angry* when I see dogs using the beach as a toilet.
- *It was such a relief* to pass my driving test.

The italicized statements all refer to feelings. Being anxious or happy or angry is not an action. We may express our relief by telephoning a friend, but there is an important distinction between feeling and action.

Thoughts

- I have great hopes for the future.
- I have enough time to get things done.
- I will always be sexually frustrated.
- I will end up living on my own.
- I am not capable of loving anyone else.

The above are not actions or feelings, they are thoughts. Thoughts are beliefs or ideas about things or people – we cannot see them in others, only infer them.

Consider how actions, feelings and thoughts all have an effect on each other. Actions influence feelings: for most of us, having a refreshing sleep (action) makes us feel better; sitting in an empty room (action) makes us feel low and lethargic. Actions influence thoughts: visiting a certain place (action) evokes vivid memories; gardening (action) makes us think of our father.

Feelings influence actions: we are feeling low so we avoid doing anything; we feel shy so we avoid a party. Feelings influence thoughts: we are feeling depressed and our mind is full of negative thoughts about things; we feel angry and we cannot stop thinking about how we have been wronged.

Thoughts influence actions: we think our partner is being unfaithful, so we rifle through their belongings; we believe our driving lesson will be awful, so we phone and cancel it. Thoughts influence feelings: when our mind is full of problems we feel tense; when we think about being on holiday we feel happy.

The foregoing helps us to differentiate between thoughts, feelings and actions. It may have become evident by now that we *cannot change the way we feel directly*.

No one can 'snap out of it'. What we *can* do is to change the ways in which we act — by rewarding positive things we do — and the ways we think — by challenging our fixed beliefs about things. In this way we change how we feel, indirectly.

"Come on, snap out of it!"

Summary

Counsellors and psychologists distinguish carefully between actions, feelings and thoughts. If we encounter a problem it is important to analyse it in terms of what we actually do, feel and think.

Review

Remind clients of the objectives listed at the beginning of this part. Have they fully *understood* and *acted upon* these? If not, return to the relevant section before proceeding.

Self-Observation

Objectives

1 To begin the process of being objective about ourselves.

2 To break down into small components what is actually happening to us.

3 To take positive action by recording what we identify.

4 To fill in a self-observation chart.

Introduction

Observing ourselves is a very difficult process. We all tend to see ourselves according to firmly entrenched prejudices, attitudes and beliefs:

- Other people look down on me.
- Things always go wrong for me.
- I will never find what I really want.

People who have personal problems find it toughest to be objective about themselves. They usually blame themselves for everything, exaggerate what is wrong about themselves whilst underestimating their good points or successes. They also only show tolerance towards the weakness of other people, never of themselves.

To facilitate self-observation we have drawn up opposite specimen charts which will act as a guide. There are examples of three fictitious situations: (1) A student at his first tutorial begins to feel panicky. His hands are sweating, his heart is racing. (2) An executive finds that the office copying machine has broken down and he screams at his secretary and slams his office door shut. (3) A housewife receives a phone call from her husband who is going to be late home. She bursts into tears.

Specimen Self-Observation Charts

THE TRIGGER What set things off? What did you or others say or do?	Arriving at the tutor's room and seeing other students waiting to go in. They were talking together.	Finding machine broken. In a rush to send off material. Boss had hinted at lunch that my dept was slow.	Have not had sex for two months. Husband moody and tired of late. Isolated at home.
What were your thoughts before your reaction?	How will I cope with these strangers?	If boss provided more staff, would I be in this rush? I would not have to do copying.	He is going to leave me for someone else.
DEALING WITH THE REACTION What were your thoughts after you had reacted?	I am going to make a fool of myself. They are more intelligent than me.	***** machine. ***** secretary. ***** company. I am going to resign.	Relax, I don't know anything for certain. It's my fault if he is unhappy. Look at me.
What did you and others do after you had reacted?	Tried to look relaxed. Concentrated on staying in control. Lit a cigarette.	Slammed door and walked out. Stood alone in office and shook. Took a Valium.	Paced up and down house. Made a cup of tea. Phoned sister.
What were your feelings (anger, sadness, guilt) once you had reacted?	Embarrassment, fear, anger at self, shame.	Anger, frustration,	Guilt, anger, fear, hopelessness, despair.
What did you say/do to make the feelings go away? Did they stop?	Said something in group. Used abdominal breathing.	Stayed on own. Apologized to secretary.	Felt better after chat with sister. Resolved to talk with husband. Resolved to find something new to do for self.

We have provided a blank self-observation chart to be completed at will. Every time a client has an unpleasant experience (for example, losing his temper, bursting into tears, giving up, hitting someone, starving himself or bingeing) he should fill in what happened in the appropriate column. Not everyone will want to do this. The easiest thing is to try and forget it, not dwell on it and get on with something else. However, ignoring the problem does not solve it. There are good reasons to observe and record behaviour:

● We cannot learn from something we are trying to forget.

● By recording what is wrong we can stop denying there is a problem.

● If we acknowledge our problems we can learn from them.

Exercise

(NB To complete this exercise satisfactorily it is essential to have worked through Chapter 1 'Minds & Bodies'.)

Find an example of your reaction to a particular event and fill in the grid below. It is important that you fill in *all* of the boxes as, later, you will

Self-Observation Chart			
	Example 1	Example 2	Example 3
The trigger			
Prior thoughts			
Thoughts about your reaction			
Your and others' actions			
Your feelings about your reactions			
Action taken to stop feelings			

© M Simmons & P Daw, 1994. This exercise may be photocopied for instructional use only.

need to try different techniques to cope with your action and thoughts. At first you may draw a blank and feel unable to remember properly the details of the situation you were in. Relax and persevere. If you focus yourself you can get beyond the blocks.

Summary

In situations where we lose our temper, have a panic attack, withdraw slightly into our shell, burst into tears and so on there is a complex range of influences affecting us. In order to 'get to the bottom of things' it is necessary to know what we actually *did*, what we were *thinking* and what we were *feeling*. It is not enough to concentrate on only one of these.

Self-observation is not an easy process but becoming more objective about ourselves is the most important step in taking control of our lives.

Review

Remind clients of the objectives listed at the beginning of this part. Have they fully *understood* and *acted upon* these? If not, return to the relevant section before proceeding.

Coping

Introduction

Everybody has ways they cope with difficult situations. For some this means avoiding them, seeing the family doctor or going out and getting drunk. For others, this involves relaxing, working on thought control and changing attitudes. Some are effective (relaxation), some are very ineffective (popping pills).

Coping strategies are behaviours, things that people do to feel better or get over something unpleasant. The seven most common strategies are:

1 Leaving/avoiding the situation.

2 Seeing a family doctor or counsellor.

3 Asking friends or relatives to help.

4 Relaxation.

5 Distraction.

6 Drugs (prescribed and non-prescribed).

7 Blaming oneself.

Leaving or avoiding ("Beam me up, Scottie")

It is a perfectly normal reaction to try and get away from something unpleasant. Only the very brave and the very foolish play the hero. Unfortunately, leaving or avoiding things quickly becomes addictive: if leaving 'works' — that is, if you feel better if you escape — you will be more likely to use it the next time you feel uncomfortable. Leaving *reinforces* the idea that this is coping. It also reinforces the idea that what you are leaving is dreadful and unchangeable.

A word about reinforcers

A reinforcer in psychology is anything which strengthens a response, or makes it more likely to occur. Simply stated, reward someone for doing something and they will do it again. This is a very powerful tool in changing our behaviour. It explains why we insisted on rewards in Chapters 1 and 2.

However, sometimes we develop bad habits and do not see the rewards: the person who comes home from work with a headache gets their dinner prepared — the headaches increase. Asking yourself "What's in this for me?" is a useful method of analysing your motives.

Leaving the situation has other consequences:

- It becomes a habit. You leave situations at the slightest sign of discomfort, until it becomes an automatic response.

- You avoid situations because you 'know you will only leave anyway'. *Anticipating* anxiety is enough to trigger an attack.

- In time you completely lose touch with certain situations or places. If you inadvertently come back into contact with them, your apprehension rises; you panic.

- Avoidance becomes a whole way of thinking. You avoid social situations, avoid decisions and try to drown your fears and feelings in excessive alcohol or drugs.

Confronting painful issues or difficult situations is not easy. We are all left with a choice between (a) the comfortable path of doing nothing, but being 'handicapped' by the discomfort of feeling awful; and (b) tolerating some pain and anguish in the hope of freeing ourselves from discomfort in the longer term.

Beware of these blocks

Yes, but …   I can't.
What's the point?   It's too difficult.
I'm a hopeless case.   I'm no good at …
If it wasn't for … then I *would* …

Seeing the family doctor

The family doctor will in most cases be an integral part of any personal programme to learn effective coping strategies (see also pages 21–26). However, it is important to be realistic about the time constraints upon doctors in today's busy surgeries. When seeking to involve a professional, it is advisable to ask for a referral to a counsellor or clinical psychologist. Alternatively, the support of a fully trained and registered therapist in the private sector should be sought.

Getting help from others

This can be a tricky path to tread. We may find our friends and family will rally round; if we can share a problem, say what we are doing to overcome difficulties and enlist their help and support, this could be a major advantage. But what is crucial is having *constructive* help, not people who take over and do everything for us. Having things done for us reinforces (by rewarding) our instinct to avoid unpleasant things and instills a sense of helplessness.

Although it might be a positive step to use the help of others, it is very important not to become *dependent* on that help. Relying on others loses rather than gains control.

Relaxation

If we are stressed, nervous, anxious or depressed, relaxation will help. The importance of incorporating a relaxation schedule in our lives cannot be emphasized enough. Relaxation works because it initially controls the physiological symptoms of anxiety.

People who panic 'over-breathe' or 'hyperventilate'. In this state they swallow gulps of air or breathe rapidly, which reduces the carbon dioxide in the blood and produces light-headedness, dizziness, tingling and accelerated heart rate. (This is covered further in Chapters 1 and 4.) These unpleasant feelings make a person feel like they are *losing control*, which makes them more anxious, breathe abnormally, and so on.

Relaxation is a learned skill. When we have learned how to relax at will we will be able to deal with physical tension more quickly and more efficiently. In time we will be able to relax even when we *anticipate* stress or threat.

Distraction

When a baby cries we wave a rattle in front of it and it is often distracted from the discomfort. It is not quite as easy with adults. For one thing, when we are feeling dreadful it is easier said than done to 'snap out of it'. For another, distractions usually involve a stimulating activity and it is not always convenient to start this when you feel the need. Furthermore, the capacity of something in particular to distract you usually decreases in time.

People who reduce their anxiety by compulsively or obsessively doing something else, for example counting, checking or performing rituals, often require intensive therapy. However, everyone has some obsessive tendencies. We all prefer to do *some* things in a certain order, to stick to certain routines. It is only when we feel there is a need to stick rigidly to routines in a way which dominates our lives that there is much cause for concern.

Drugs

Part 4 of Chapter 1 has looked at an approach to handling prescribed medication. Drugs are a complex issue because they involve both physical and psychological dependency. Remember these points:

- talk to your family doctor and enlist his/her support;
- collect the facts;
- make a plan — do not leave things to chance;
- reward your successes generously;
- treat setbacks as such and not as irredeemable failures.

Exercise

Running ourselves down or using negative thoughts (see page 47) is a common response to having a problem.

- I must be liked by everyone.
- It is better to please others than myself.
- I must be perfect in everything I attempt to do.
- I have little control in what happens to me.
- I cannot change how I am.
- Anger is bad and should never be expressed.

To agree with any of these statements indicates we are *not talking sensibly to ourselves.*

If we set ourselves impossibly high standards for living then we will inevitably end up frustrated, resentful, angry and dissatisfied with ourselves. These high and *unrealistic* standards need to be challenged. Must we be liked by *everyone*? Do we *always* have to be perfect? Asking ourselves to be super-beings introduces a high sense of personal failure when things go wrong. In other words, we blame ourselves rather than maintaining a sense of proportion and balance.

Write down four thoughts you commonly have which are negative or self-blaming, for example: "I am not capable of loving"; "I am worthless." Now write these statements into the left-hand column of the grid below. In the right-hand side of the grid rewrite your original statement in more positive terms.

Negative Statement	Positive Alternative
I am not capable of loving	Okay, I have had some bad relationships, but I'm working on not messing things up again.
I am worthless	I might fail sometimes, but in some ways I am quite competent.
1...	
2...	
3...	
4...	

Summary

Ask clients to write, as in the example below, the methods they currently use for coping with stress, problems, difficulties, moods or nerves. Alongside each method score the effectiveness of this measure on a scale of one to 10. Thus, if they think getting drunk is very effective, they might give it a score of eight. (If they think that getting drunk warrants a score of eight, we are not getting through!)

Problem	Coping method used	Effectiveness (1–10)
Anxious about attending night school	Putting self to bed	1

The aim is to increase effective coping methods and decrease ineffective methods. This takes time, but is worth the effort if tackled in small, achievable steps.

Review

Remind clients of the objectives listed at the beginning of this part. Have they fully *understood* and *acted upon* these? If not, return to the relevant section before proceeding.

Understanding Others & Understanding Ourselves

Objectives

1 To understand the dynamics of defence mechanisms.

2 To consider ways in which others relate to us.

3 To reappraise our own methods of interacting with others.

Introduction

Nobody likes to feel pain. Just as our reflexes protect us from sources of physical pain, such as extreme heat, so we learn to protect ourselves from psychological pain. This learning process commences in childhood when pain and hurt are more often than not locked away rather than openly expressed. Sigmund Freud was the first to suggest that in adulthood we use specific strategies to shield ourselves from pain. This pain is buried in our past and either reminds us of or represents something about ourselves in the present which we do not like and find unacceptable.

In this part we aim to present a brief explanation of these mechanisms. Trying to understand how we deal with others, and how others deal with us, gives us a solid platform for self-exploration.

Key concepts

Suppression

Feelings we are not comfortable with are swallowed. For example, a mother who feels resentful of the demands of her child but unable to face up to the reasons and consequences of such feelings buries them. Similarly, a stressed businessman who is criticized by his boss does not allow himself to show his feelings in this situation.

Repression

This is similar to suppression but more complex. Repressed feelings often derive from childhood and involve not only burying the feelings but actually forgetting the feelings are there: in suppression, we lock our fears in the cellar; in repression we throw away the key. Both suppression and repression involve the process of denial, which may be conscious or unconscious.

The unconscious

The unconscious is where all our painful, upsetting memories are stored. Trying to keep all our 'nasty' feelings hidden is like trying to keep a ball under water — every so often, when we are not concentrating, it shoots up to the surface. Psychoanalysis holds that we need to understand the contents of the unconscious to function as a healthy person.

How can we know if buried memories and stored pain are exerting an influence on our lives? Let us consider the concepts below and think about them in the context of our lives.

Displacement

Every time we kick the cat, we are displacing our unexpressed needs and feelings: one feature of displacement is that we are always taking things out on someone who is less powerful than ourselves.

Consider the case of the stressed businessman. He comes home from a day of pressure and tension in which he failed to get the promotion he was hoping for. He becomes furious over the fact that his supper is cold. This seems to be an overreaction (especially as it is salad). What is he really feeling? Probably his need to be cared for is not really being met. But this feeling and the anger that goes with it does not really apply to his wife; rather it applies to his boss. So he has displaced the feeling. The anger that he felt at the time towards his boss is being held back by suppression. The businessman has blocked his feelings, in this instance for fear of jeopardizing his job.

However, this may not be all of the story. The anger that he shows to his wife might really apply to one of his parents who paid him no attention when he was a child. In his childhood he repressed his frustration at his parents, but the experience with his boss elicited these feelings.

Denying our feelings is a recipe for displacement or showing substitute feelings which we think are more appropriate. Interestingly, important differences exist in this process between men and women. Our culture approves of different types of emotional expression in men and women. Women are brought up to express feelings of guilt and sadness, yet suppress anger. Conversely, men are brought up to express feelings of anger, yet suppress guilt or sadness. Thus, if a woman denies angry feelings, they may emerge as sadness, or, if a man suppresses guilty feelings, they may come out as anger.

Projection

This key idea is like displacement, in that it involves putting a feeling where it does not belong. In addition to this, however, projection involves how we express our self-image. Our self-image is built through childhood and adolescence. The image we show to the world is called the *ego* and represents those parts of us that we find acceptable. Conversely, those parts we find frightening and unattractive are split off and buried away in the unconscious. These parts have been called the *shadow*.

For example, a person accuses their partner of being moody when in fact they are unwilling to recognize their own moodiness; that is, they project themselves outwards. Or someone becomes upset when they hear someone else spreading rumours. They probably dislike the gossip inside themselves. When people complain about other people it is often the case that they are unconsciously describing themselves! Have we ever wondered why people protest too much?

A more complex example is given below.

Case History

Miss H spent much of her adult life consciously caring for her cantankerous mother. She sacrificed opportunities of marriage and of friendship, yet not once did she complain about the way her mother used and even abused her. After her mother died, Miss H gave up going to the shops, gave up going out at all, becoming more and more afraid of the outside world, believing it to be populated entirely by muggers and rapists. Of course she was grieving for her mother and for the life that she never had, but also she was projecting her hatred of her mother onto the outside world. Her anger at her mother was surfacing and she could not bear to face it, having always been told that she must not have feelings like that. She had to place this feeling somewhere, so she imagined it belonged with the outside world — that the outside world and the people in it were hostile and full of hatred. It was through long, intensive therapy, beyond the scope of this book, that she was finally able to acknowledge these feelings towards her mother and come to accept the most difficult psychological conflict that any of us have to contend with — that of loving and hating the same person at the same time.

This case history should be considered carefully. Perhaps the client can think of situations when others project onto them? How does it feel? When do they project onto others? They may not be like Miss H, but it will be helpful for them to be aware of the process.

Introjection

This refers to taking in the projections of other people. It is particularly noticeable in families when children introject (absorb) the opinions and judgements (projections) of their parents. Consider the family relationships and dynamics of X, Y and Z:

- X, the grandfather, is strict and an inflexible disciplinarian who demands the highest standards from his eldest daughter, Y.

- Y grows up in fear of her incompetence, because of her father, X, and, rather than admit to her own weaknesses, she projects them onto others, particularly her son, Z.

- Z is consistently criticized as a child and learns to think that he is stupid and incompetent.

In this example Z's opportunities and potential are stunted by his belief that he is stupid. In fact he has introjected his mother's projections and needs to learn to be himself. Such concepts need not be confusing. They can help us to understand more fully the dynamics of our own family life.

As we start changing ourselves, we will in turn be changing the dynamics of our relationships. A change in one person upsets the status quo in a relationship or family. Others who are close to us go on behaving towards us in the same old way and expect us to do the same with them. Our changing patterns of behaviour therefore inevitably upset their patterns of behaviour. If they are not ready for or do not welcome the changes that we are making in ourselves, they may try, consciously or unconsciously, to sabotage our attempts to change. Others may do this by expecting more of us, increasing the pressure upon us to stay the same, or by withdrawing.

For example, as we rid ourselves of depression, we may also question and reject introjections that we have made in the past. If we had introjected others' opinions about our worthlessness, then, as we slough these off, others who are close to us may increase their projection upon us of such views. An example of this might be the housewife and mother who, having been brought up to believe that her only worth resides in looking after others and that otherwise she is incompetent, through the encouragement of a friend takes driving lessons, buys a car and attends car maintenance classes. Her relationship with her husband needs to change accordingly, but he is reluctant to acknowledge her growing independence, preferring to think of her as dependent and, in matters outside the home and children, as incompetent. He thus continues to project onto his wife his anxiety about his own inadequacy in the outside world and tries to dominate her further, through criticism and control. Clearly he needs to change as well, to recognize and express his own doubts about his competence and come to terms with his own real inadequacies.

Changing ourselves always involves changing the nature of our relationships. We must therefore be prepared for this and, best of all, prepare our family and friends in order to help them begin to adjust to us.

Summary

In this section we have learned about the self-defence mechanisms of:

- displacement,
- repression,
- introjection.
- denial,
- splitting,
- suppression,
- projection,

We need to rely on scrupulous honesty if these concepts are to help give us greater insight into the way we relate to others, and others relate to us. Honesty about ourselves is not easy but it is a prerequisite to successfully working through our personal difficulties and problems.

Review

Remind clients of the objectives listed at the beginning of this part. Have they fully *understood* and *acted upon* these? If not, return to the relevant section before proceeding.

Conclusions

Trying to understand what 'makes us tick' is a difficult problem. We live inside our own minds, surrounded by our thoughts and feelings. At school nobody taught us how to sort through all of this. And when we suffer from personal problems it is imperative that we try to become objective about ourselves. This means being able to answer three basic questions.

1 What am I doing?

2 What am I thinking?

3 What am I feeling?

When we experience a problem, what are we doing, thinking and feeling before, during and after it?

How do we cope at present? In all likelihood we cope by avoiding, seeking oblivion, by denying, by telling ourselves that tomorrow is another day and all our problems will magically disappear. If this was true why are they still hanging around today?

By the time that the client has worked through this chapter we hope that he will have:

- learned to separate his experience into actions, feelings and thoughts;

- appraised his present coping strategies and planned better ones;

- analysed the specifics of his problems rather than letting them go in a vague haze he would sooner ignore and forget.

In addition to this he has been asked to consider which unconscious processes are coming to bear in his relationships with others. He will be beginning to learn what 'makes him tick'. He is beginning to understand how to be objective about himself. Having developed a feel for the ideas and concepts of therapy, he no longer needs to feel intimidated by the process:

- He is in control.

- He is not practising 'mumbo-jumbo'.

- He is systematically working on changing his life, using established psychological techniques.

Armed with this knowledge we are ready to proceed.

An Anxiety Management Programme

4

Objectives

1 To review what the anxiety response is.

2 To discover why it is linked to certain situations.

3 To examine the cycle of physiology, thought and behaviour which creates and maintains anxiety.

4 To learn methods to break this cycle by physical means.

5 To learn methods to break this cycle by thinking differently.

6 To learn how to apply these methods to the situations which cause our anxiety.

What is anxiety?

- Anxiety, like fear, is an emotion.
- It is part of a biological survival mechanism.
- Everyone experiences anxiety.
- It is a normal and totally necessary human function.
- It tells us that something is a threat to our survival.
- It motivates us to confront or avoid the threat.
- It is sometimes called the 'fight or flight' response.
- It is a response to stress.
- Mostly people experience anxiety or fear as an overwhelming desire to get away from the situation.

Stress or anxiety?

In the popular media stress and anxiety are often mistakenly used interchangeably. Stress, as covered in Part 1 of Chapter 2, represents the external and/or internal forces acting upon an individual. Anxiety, on the other hand, is a response to those forces.

As we have seen in Part 2 of Chapter 1, the anxiety response is controlled by a part of the nervous system. Unlike the part of the nervous system that governs limb movement, it can be entirely automatic and to a considerable extent beyond our control. Thus it is called the autonomic nervous system; it comprises two parts, the sympathetic and parasympathetic nervous systems. The sympathetic system prepares us for action in the face of possible danger. The parasympathetic system acts to redress the balance once the crisis has passed.

The physical reactions of the anxiety response are set out below:

Sympathetic	Parasympathetic
Dilates pupils	Constricts pupils
Inhibits saliva flow	Increases saliva flow
Raises heartbeat	Slows heartbeat
Dilates bronchial tubes	Constricts bronchial tubes
Inhibits peristalsis	Stimulates peristalsis
Inhibits gastric secretion	Stimulates gastric secretion
Inhibits bladder contraction	Constricts the bladder
Stimulates adrenaline secretion	

We have seen that there is an optimum amount of anxiety for survival in any given situation. Recall the inverted U-shaped graph on page 29. Too little anxiety may be fatal, too much and we can become paralysed like a rabbit in the car headlights.

Some fears and anxieties are more rational, such as fear of heights, surgical operations, or losing loved ones. Some are less rational, such as fear of spiders, crowds, or eating in public. In all cases, however, it is the *amount* of anxiety felt that is the issue — whether it is *proportional to the reality of the threat* posed by the situation.

Fear

Fear can be distinguished from anxiety. Fear is focused upon specific objects or situations (such as snakes, supermarket queues or hypodermic needles) and occurs in their proximity. It is often called a *phobia* when it occurs in relation to a specific object or situation.

On the other hand, anxiety occurs in *anticipation* of such situations or may be a much more general feeling without a specific focus, occurring at random, when it is called 'free-floating' or generalized anxiety. In the extreme, both anxiety and fear can build up to produce 'panic attacks', when the cycle of responses of body, thought and behaviour goes out of control.

It is important to realize that this biological response is in essence the same as that experienced by other animals. However, in humans, who have the power of thought and conceptualization, the ability to anticipate fear or anxiety itself becomes part of the cycle of anxiety and makes the problem more complex.

At this point the client should be asked to make a list of all the physical feelings he experiences when he is anxious. Then he can make a list of all the physical feelings he has when he is relaxed.

Why does anxiety occur?

These days there are many more complex causes of anxiety than simple threats to biological survival. Stresses ranging from getting to work, meeting deadlines, organizing our everyday lives and making personal choices, on the one hand, to worrying about the greenhouse effect and nuclear war, on the other, mean that the load upon our capacity to handle stress is greater than ever before. As we have seen in Chapter 2, our individual capacity to cope with pressures varies according to our personal resources, the way we organize ourselves and the supportiveness of our relationships. These can be increased but our capacity to handle pressure is *finite* and, when that capacity is exceeded, we may experience acute anxiety. So we need to learn to (a) reduce the pressures upon ourselves and (b) cope better with the pressures we cannot reduce.

An analogy for the way we handle pressure would be a tumbler which is being filled from several taps. We are trying to stop the water overflowing or spilling straight out of the taps. That overflow is like a panic attack. So we either turn off some of the taps or drink some of the water from the tumbler. Turning off a tap or two is like reducing the amount of stress entering our lives; drinking the water is like coping better with the stresses. In practice we need to use *both* of these methods to reduce our anxiety.

Anxiety may be generated when there is a deeply felt but *often unconscious* need to change things about our lives. Under these circumstances this need may be accompanied by impulses and feelings which we do not acknowledge but which cause us anxiety as they come nearer to the surface.

'Free-floating' or generalized anxiety may arise by this mechanism or it may be the result of a range of behavioural habits which maintain high physiological arousal, such as rushing about, failing to relax, or drinking lots of coffee, plus cognitive habits, such as irrational perfectionist beliefs, faulty interpretation of events, or negative automatic thoughts. (See Chapter 2, Part 1.)

We may, however, experience anxiety as being associated with particular situations or events. Apart from those situations where anxiety is a response to an actual threat to our survival, there are three main ways in which anxiety becomes associated with specific objects or situations.

Trauma

When an event is very traumatic, fear becomes very strongly linked with the situation or significant objects within it. An example of this process is something that most of us will have experienced. If we have had a car crash or a narrow escape on the road, subsequently we will feel more or less anxious when we drive past the place where the accident occurred.

Imitation

The second main way in which anxiety becomes associated with particular objects, situations or activities is through a process called social learning. This process is also called modelling, for in it we 'model' our attitudes and behaviours upon those of people who are particularly important to us, such as our parents. This process is particularly important in childhood, for to a child's mind her parents are all-powerful. If *they* are afraid of something then it must be really scary.

An example of this process is the fear of the dark of an adult whose parents, when she was a child, always slept with the lights on. In this case her parents will have initiated and maintained the idea that the dark was frightening quite unintentionally, thus passing on their own anxieties about it.

Reinforcement

The third main way in which anxiety becomes associated with particular objects, situations or activities is through the action of reinforcement. This process is responsible for the maintenance and development of anxiety associations. This is how it works. Recall the example of the car crash, given earlier, and the creation of the association between the place where the accident occurred and feelings of fear. If we regularly continue to pass the place without further incident, the anxiety associated with it will fade. If, however, we *avoid* the place after the accident, we will avoid initial anxiety, but the association between the place and the emotion of fear will remain as strong as it was immediately after the incident. Furthermore, our avoidance will be reinforced by the temporary relief from the anxiety we get by avoiding the situation.

In other words, if we experience relief from anxiety by avoiding a situation we fear, we are rewarding our avoidance. *But to overcome anxiety we must confront situations we fear*.

At this point the client should make a list of the changes in his life that may be making him anxious. Next he makes a list of all the situations, activities or objects that make him feel anxious. Finally, he makes a list of all the situations and so on that may make others anxious but in which he keeps calm.

How does anxiety occur?

We have seen earlier that there are three main elements of the overall system that create the experience of anxiety: the physical, the cognitive and the behavioural. These three types of function combine to make a cycle that often feels extremely vicious. Let us examine how the cycle works. (Reference to Chapter 2, Part 1 will help to explain the process.)

1 We *perceive* an event. We may be especially sensitive to certain types of event (hypersensitivity) or especially on the lookout for them (hypervigilance) if these types of event have precipitated an anxiety response in the past.

2 We *interpret* the event as threatening.

3 We *think* about what our interpretation of the event means for us. These thoughts may be rational (in the case of a real threat) or distorted, as characterized by negative automatic thoughts.

4 Our sympathetic nervous system *reacts*, to give us the symptoms of anxiety and fear. Then the process of becoming anxious can itself cause further anxiety. This is known as *secondary anxiety* and is fundamental to the development of *panic*.

5 We notice the symptoms of anxiety and think negative automatic thoughts such as, "Oh no, here it is again", "Oh God, I can't stand it", "All those people are watching me", "They must think I'm mad", or "I'm going to die." In this way we perceive our bodies as betraying us, our physiological anxiety response itself being a threat to us.

6 Our panicky thoughts feed back into the cycle of anxiety, thereby increasing our physiological symptoms.

7 We take *avoiding* action. We run, we hide. All we can do is obey the imperative to get away (see page 68).

8 The parasympathetic nervous system begins to take over our body again. We feel enormous relief. We have thus *reinforced* or rewarded our behaviour in escaping from the situation but already, in this wave of relief, we are worrying about the next time that we will have to confront our anxiety.

Physical methods of control

So let us do something about this. In the past we will have tried to keep ourselves calm and distract ourselves from our anxious thoughts and feelings, but, without a system, these noble efforts may not have accounted for much. Our first task is to tackle some of the physiological responses to anxiety.

First, the client sits down in an upright chair on his own. He takes one very deep breath. He holds his breath and, while doing so, concentrates upon where in his body he feels tension. It may be in his neck and shoulders; it may be in his hands; it may be in his stomach and diaphragm. Having held his breath until he cannot hold it any longer, the client lets all his breath out in a short sharp explosion. As he lets his breath out, he should notice how the tension dissolves a little. Then he goes back to breathing normally. This preliminary exercise is useful for finding out where a person holds the tension in their body and is a useful quick release technique.

If the client is over-breathing or hyperventilating when anxious, see Chapter 1, Part 1. The third step is deep relaxation. This is used to get rid of the tension which, unknown to us, builds up during the day. Over the long term, relaxation also acts in a preventive way. It is one of the basic building-blocks of this Anxiety Management Programme. Learning to use deep relaxation is a matter of learning to recognize what it feels like when muscles are tense and then learning to let that tension go. This is the key to relaxation — we cannot *make* ourselves relax, we *let* ourselves relax.

Suggested relaxation exercises

Sit or lie down in a comfortable position. Close your eyes. Relax yourself to the best of your ability, then tackle the following exercises. Each time, tense the muscles for five seconds, then slowly relax them for about 15 seconds. Pay close attention to the sensations you feel when you have tensed up and when you relax. Try to identify where the feelings of the tension occur. After each exercise, let the relaxation spread over the whole body. Concentrate on using *abdominal breathing* throughout. Initially, you should devote about 30 minutes a day to these exercises.

Phase I	
Clench your right fist	Note the tension in your fingers, hands and forearm. Repeat with other fist.
Bend your elbow and tense your bicep muscle	Note the tension. Relax. Repeat with other arm.
Straighten your arm so you feel most tension in the tricep muscles along the back of your arm	Note the tension. Relax. Repeat with other arm.

Phase II

Facial area

Wrinkle your forehead	Note the tension. Relax and 'smooth out' your forehead.
Frown and crease your brows	Note the tension. Relax and 'smooth out' your forehead again. Picture your entire forehead and scalp becoming smoother as relaxation increases.
Screw up your eyes	Note the tension. Relax.
Wrinkle your nose	Note the tension. Relax.
Clench your jaws and bite your teeth together	Note the tension. Relax and let your lips part slightly.
Press your tongue against the roof of your mouth	Note the tension. Relax.
Purse your lips, press your lips together very tightly	Note the tension. Relax.

Neck

Press your head back as far as possible	Note the tension.
Roll it to the right	Feel the tension shift.
Roll it to the left	Feel the tension shift.
Straighten your head, bring it forward and press your chin against your chest.	Note the tension. Return your head to a comfortable position and relax.

Shoulders and upper back

Shrug your shoulders	Note the tension. Drop your shoulders and relax.
Shrug your shoulders, move them forward and back	Note the tension. Relax.

Phase III

Chest

Breathe in deeply	Hold it. Note the tension. Exhale and relax.

Stomach

Push your stomach out and make your abdomen hard	Note the tension. Relax.
Draw your stomach in (as if anticipating a punch)	Note the tension.

Lower back

Arch your back, make your lower back quite hollow	Note the tension. Relax.

Phase IV

Buttocks, hips and thighs

Press your heels down as hard as you can and flex your thighs	Note the tension and relax.
Straighten your knees and flex your thighs	Note the tension. Relax.

Calves and shins

Straighten your legs, point your toes and feet downwards, away from your face, so that your calf muscles tense	Note the tension. Relax.
Straighten your legs, point your toes and feet towards your face so that you feel tension along your shins	Note the tension. Relax.

Ankles, feet and toes

Rotate your foot from the ankle	Note the tension. Relax.
Bend or clench your toes within your shoe	Note the tension. Relax.

When the exercises have been completed, let yourself slip deeper and deeper into relaxation. Maintain abdominal breathing, noticing how heavy and relaxed you have become. Keep on relaxing.

When you wish to get up, count backwards from four to zero. Open your eyes. You should feel refreshed and calm.

We recommend the use of a deep relaxation cassette tape for learning progressive muscle relaxation. The advantage of using a tape is that you do not have to try to remember what to do. Instead you are able to concentrate as fully as possible on the exercises themselves and the growing feelings of relaxation. The authors have produced a tape for which there is an order form at the end of the book.

Deep Relaxation Programme

A Set aside at least one (preferably two) regular periods of 30 minutes every day for practice when you can guarantee no disturbance (unplug the telephone) and when you will feel fairly relaxed anyway. A relaxation tape is a great help.

B Choose to relax on your bed or in an armchair with a head support, whichever you prefer. If you have problems in sleeping at night, it may be wise to practise deep relaxation on your bed in the evening.

C Keep your breathing regular and shallow. Try not to hold your breath as you tighten and relax each muscle.

D Carry out each movement as smoothly as you can.

E If distracting thoughts or sensations come into your mind (as they surely will), do not worry because this is completely natural. Just try not to concentrate upon them but let them recede from your mind and concentrate instead on your body and the word *relax.*

F Do not concern yourself with how well you are performing the deep relaxation technique. This is not a task that you 'must get right'. As already mentioned, trying actively to relax does not work. Just *let it happen* and concentrate on the word 'relax' and upon the rhythm of your breathing.

G After your relaxation tape has ended, stay sitting or lying quietly for a few minutes and then get up slowly in your own time. Try to avoid rushing about for half an hour.

H Practise deep relaxation every day for two weeks before proceeding further into this programme.

After the client has been practising deep relaxation regularly for two weeks, he will be feeling more skilled and confident about it. Now we are ready to build up an association between the feelings of relaxation and a particular cue word.

The purpose of the cue word is to enable the client eventually to summon up the feelings of relaxation at a moment's notice, for instance when he is in a situation which creates anxiety for him. He should choose a word which best signifies for him the feeling of relaxation. It might be 'relax', though people have chosen a variety of words such as 'calm', 'peace' or 'serene'. Now, when he practises deep relaxation, he says his cue word to himself *each time* he releases the tension from his muscles. In this way a strong association will be built between feelings of relaxation and the cue word. The client should make sure of this strong association before using the cue word to relax himself in an anxiety-producing situation — about two weeks should do it.

Detailed instructions on abdominal breathing are to be found on pages 3–5. The client should start by practising it every day *only* during quiet, relaxed moments. Remind him that the key ideas are (a) concentrate on the movement of your abdomen and the flow of your breath; (b) relax your shoulders and chest a little with each breath; (c) when you are distracted by thoughts and sensations, notice them, let them go and bring your mind back to the movement of your abdomen and the flow of your breath.

The client should try to complete five sessions of five minutes each day, and incorporate them into his relaxation sessions. When this method of breathing feels natural and easy (this may be after a week or two of regular practice) then he is ready to apply it when he feels anxious. For the first week of applying it, he should try to use it only in less intense situations, such as when he is anticipating what is making him anxious, rather than hoping it will work in a full-blown panic attack. It will eventually, but he needs to build up his confidence in the technique first.

Although he is now applying abdominal breathing to anxiety-producing situations, it is crucial that the client continue to practise it regularly and frequently at times of greater calmness. This helps to maintain its association with feelings of relaxation.

Psychological methods of control

We have now learned how to do deep relaxation, how to produce the feelings of relaxation on demand by using our cue word and how to reduce the physical feelings of anxiety and to distract ourselves from them by using abdominal breathing. Having incorporated these skills into our daily routine, it is now time for us to learn the ways to overcome anxiety by thinking differently.

There are two main ways in which thought can affect our emotions. One is through imagery, or the pictures we create in our minds. The other is through verbal self-statements, or the sentences we say to ourselves. The client now tries the following exercise to discover the effects of *negative* imagery upon what he feels.

Exercise

In a quiet setting, spend a minute or so imagining a situation in which you feel particularly anxious. Imagine it in greater and greater detail. Don't just picture it but listen to the sounds and smell the smells.

What do you feel? You feel anxious! Now that was hard, we know. But there was a point in putting you through that. It was to show you how powerful your thoughts are in immediately creating feelings. If your thoughts can create bad feelings that easily, you can imagine what a powerful force they could be in producing good feelings.

Relaxing image

Here we learn to use the power of imagery to increase feelings of relaxation. In the same quiet setting, imagine yourself back in a situation in the past that you found particularly relaxing. For many people, holiday memories, especially those times of lying on the beach in the sun, are favourite. Others have chosen memories of picnics, concerts or even soaking in a nice warm bath.

Choose a memory that for you best summons up those comfortable, relaxed feelings. If you really cannot remember anything, then choose an image that you think will be relaxing. Now, after each deep relaxation practice, continue to lie or sit there for five minutes or so and take your mind into the relaxing image that you have chosen. Remember the sights, look around yourself in your mind's eye. Remember the sounds, hear them now. Remember the feelings, the warmth of the sun on your skin, the feel of your own body. Remember the smells in the air and the tastes on your tongue.

You will be surprised at just how much detail you are able to create in your mind by looking and listening closer and closer in your imagination. If during your sessions of relaxing image practice you find yourself losing concentration, just look in another direction or look more closely and create more detail in your mind's eye. It does not matter if your creative imagination influences what you are remembering; in fact that is exactly what is wanted.

After you have practised producing your relaxing image every day for two weeks, you are ready to start applying it to situations of anticipatory anxiety: combined with abdominal breathing and your cue word in the dentist's waiting room awaiting your appointment, for example.

Competent image

As well as using imagery to produce feelings of relaxation, we can use it effectively to increase feelings of confidence. Just as you did when you built up your relaxing image, find a quiet place and time when you can give your thoughts over to concentrating upon a situation in which you feel *competent*.

Identify and concentrate upon a situation or an area in which you do feel confident in your ability. It might be driving your car, some particular aspect of your work, your achievements in being a parent, a hobby, a sport or other interest. What counts is that the situation you choose for your competent image really does reflect a situation in which you feel confident of your ability or achievement, however small that may be.

Develop your competent image over two weeks in exactly the same way as you developed your relaxing image. Remember to include the senses of hearing, touch, smell and taste as far as you can. Although it is helpful to start by developing your competent image at the end of your deep relaxation sessions, it is not necessary to stick to these times only.

After all, unlike your relaxing image, your competent image may not be tranquil and peaceful. For example, your hobby may be rally driving!

If, no matter how hard you try, you simply cannot imagine yourself in a competent role of any sort then develop your competent image by thinking of a friend, as similar to you as possible and who, like you, has their own difficulties, handling a situation competently. After developing this image at the end of a few deep relaxation sessions substitute yourself for your friend in your mind's eye.

After developing both your competent image and your relaxing image you can choose which to use according to the situation and your feelings within it. You will be the best judge of which to use and when.

Self-statements

As already mentioned, the other way in which thoughts affect feelings is in what we say to ourselves — self-statements. Without our controlling these, they are generally negative, particularly in an anxiety-producing situation. We gave as an example earlier the type of panicky self-statements that we make when we are anxious: "Oh no, here it is again", "Oh God, I can't stand it", "They must think I'm mad", "I can't bear it", and so on.

Exercise

Make a list of all the negative self-statements you make when you are in or anticipating an anxiety–producing situation. To make it easier to think of these negative self-statements, imagine yourself in an anxiety-producing situation as in the exercise on page 93.

Example: "What if I'm sick in public?"

1

2

3

4

5

6

7

We will see that the statements we have written above are all unhelpful, because they contribute further to a build-up of anxiety. This is because they create the *expectancy* that the anxiety will get worse — and so it does.

By now we have learned a lot about anxiety: what it is, why it happens, how it occurs and how to overcome it using both physical and mental methods. In fact we are becoming an expert on the subject and we need no longer fear so much something that we are beginning to understand. So do we need those old negative self-statements, with their negative expectancies, any more? Do they fit in with our understanding of anxiety and experience of controlling it? By now we will have new *positive* expectancies. Perhaps our self-statements could reflect these.

Exercise

Look at the following examples of positive, coping self-statements replacing negative ones. Then write your own negative self-statements from the previous exercise into the spaces provided and generate your own positive coping self-statements to replace each of them.

1 "Oh no, here it comes again."
THIS IS JUST ANXIETY; EVEN IF I DO NOTHING IT WILL SUBSIDE AFTER ABOUT 20 MINUTES.

2 "It's getting worse."
WHAT IS IT THAT I HAVE TO DO? RELAXATION, CUE WORD, ABDOMINAL BREATHING.

3 "Oh God, I can't stand it."
I'M NOT GOING TO LET WORRIES TAKE OVER — I CAN DECIDE WHAT TO THINK ABOUT. I'LL THINK ABOUT THE TIMES I'VE MANAGED REASONABLY BEFORE.

4 "I'm so stupid, everybody else is all right."
YES. I'M FEELING ANXIOUS. THAT MAKES ME HUMAN, NOT STUPID. I AM NOT HELPLESS. I AM LEARNING TO COPE. I'LL USE MY ANXIETY MANAGEMENT PLAN NOW.

5 "Everyone is looking; they must think I'm mad."	LOOK AROUND. EXAMINE THE FACTS. IS ANYONE LOOKING AT ME? EVEN IF THEY ARE, I CAN'T POSSIBLY KNOW WHAT THEY ARE THINKING.
6 "I've got to get out."	STOP! COUNT DOWN FROM 10 TO NOUGHT. NOW USE MY COPING METHODS — RELAXATION, CUE WORD, ABDOMINAL BREATHING.
7 "I'm going to die."	MY BODY IS JUST RESPONDING TO ANXIETY. IT WON'T HURT ME. THE ANXIETY WILL SOON BE OVER.

1 ....

2 ....

3 ....

4 ....

5 ....

6 ....

7 ....

Now that we have a set of positive coping self-statements it is necessary to practise them so that it is easy to remember to say them to ourselves when we are in an anxiety-producing situation. Some people like to write them down on a card and keep them in their pocket or handbag. If we practise our new positive self-statements before we do our regular abdominal breathing practice, we will feel confident about remembering them.

Applying anxiety management methods

The client now has a considerable armoury of methods at his disposal to combat anxiety. This section is about how to put them into practice. On page 105 you will find a chart showing a complete anxiety management programme. Please ask your clients to use this chart as they plan and implement their own programme. It plots the incremental use in eight stages of all the anxiety management techniques described in this chapter. Each stage should last for at least a week, but possibly as long as four weeks, depending upon the severity and duration of the anxiety problem.

As with any newly acquired set of skills, it is most wise to put them into practice slowly, without making large demands on them straight away. This is the principle behind the procedure of *graduated exposure*. In this the client will expose himself to his particular anxiety-producing situations in a gradual, ordered way that we programme in advance. This does not mean that he will not experience any feelings of anxiety at all. He will, but in small, manageable amounts.

To apply our newly acquired methods, we first need to create a staircase of anxiety-producing situations with levels or treads of increasing difficulty.

Constructing a staircase

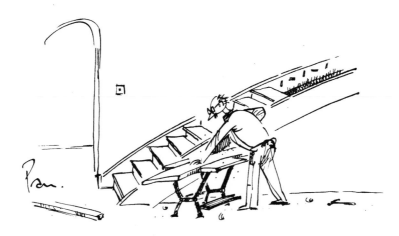

After we have built it, we will slowly walk down this staircase. Looking down it from the top, the situations on each tread will seem increasingly difficult and increasingly anxiety-provoking. But there are four key things to remember:

1 There need to be as many treads as possible.
2 These need to be as close to each other as possible.

3 The longer we spend on each tread, the wider it becomes and the more secure we will feel upon it.

4 The situation on each tread needs to be as precisely defined as possible:

- WHERE are we?
- WHEN are we there?
- WHO is with us?
- WHAT are we doing?
- HOW LONG for?

The top tread of the staircase is where we will feel no anxiety. This will be number 0. The bottom tread of the staircase represents the most feared situation that we would like to be able to achieve. This will be number 100.

Example: A person who is afraid of spiders might construct a staircase thus:

0 Mid-morning, sitting in the lounge with the door closed, with Jenny, with a picture of a spider in the next room, for 20 minutes.

5 Mid-morning, sitting in the lounge with the door open, with Jenny, with the picture of a spider on the other side of the lounge, for 20 minutes.

10 Lunchtime, sitting in the lounge with the door open, on my own, with the picture of the spider on the other side of the lounge, for 20 minutes.

15 Lunchtime, sitting in the lounge with the door closed, with Jenny, with a small dead spider in the other room, for 20 minutes.

20–25 etc all the way up to —

95 Evening, in the bathroom wearing rubber gloves, on my own, clasping a large live spider in my hands, for 5 minutes. Then dropping it out of the window.

100 Evening, in the bathroom, on my own, with bare hands picking a large spider out of the bath, walking slowly to the window and dropping it out.

Now it is the client's turn to construct his own staircase. If he has more than one type of anxiety-producing situation it is best only to tackle one type at a time and to make different staircases for different types of fear. For example, if he is anxious about spiders, like the person in the previous example, but is also anxious about being out in crowded places, these anxieties will need to be tackled separately, with separate staircases.

Before he starts, he should consider carefully the factors influencing his anxiety, for better or worse, in the type of situation that he will be tackling. It is no use closing our eyes and simply hoping for the best — it does not work.

- Does company help?
- Is the company of some people more helpful than that of others?
- Does the time of day make a difference?
- Is his anxiety in the situation better or worse by day or night?
- Is the amount of time spent in the situation important?
- Is it easier to spend more time or less time?
- Where he is in relation to the thing he is anxious about is obviously an important factor — this is the principle behind the staircase.
- What he is doing in the situation is crucial. In the past he has been generating a cycle of anxiety. Now he will be generating a cycle of coping and relaxation.

These are called the *parameters* of the levels of the staircase and might be thought of as the measurements of the treads and risers. It will be necessary to juggle these parameters in order to ensure a very *gentle* transition between one tread and the next. So, before he starts to construct his staircase, the client should be reminded to define each tread precisely according to the parameters of where, when, who with, what he is doing and for how long.

It will be necessary for him to make one or two rough copies before copying the final version of his staircase onto the form provided (page 104) and because he may also need to change the parameters of his final version as he progresses down it, we suggest that he writes on the form in pencil.

Filling in the staircase

The client starts with level 0, an anxiety-producing situation but one in which he feels negligible anxiety. Next he goes to the opposite extreme — 100. He is asked to think of a situation that he would like to be able to handle calmly but which provokes the greatest feeling of anxiety. This will not be pleasant, but it must be done, so the client's chosen anxiety management methods should be used now so that he may keep calm while he defines the situation.

Next, he should try to identify and define a situation which is half-way between 0 and 100; that is, a situation which produces 50 per cent anxiety. Having done that, he identifies and defines a situation half-way between 0 and 50 — 25 per cent anxiety; then a situation half-way between 50 and 100 — 75 per cent anxiety. Now he has five levels fixed upon his scale.

The client continues to identify and define at least ten more steps, remembering to pay attention to where, when, who with, what he does and for how long. When he has enough levels, well enough defined and smoothly enough graduated, he enters them in pencil on the form.

Walking down the staircase

The client will probably find himself starting at a level further on than 0; maybe it will be at 20–25! This is the level at which he is already operating, although with some anxiety. Some very brave souls may be functioning even further down the staircase, but at the cost of feeling great anxiety. The client must decide on which tread he wants to start. We suggest a level at which he feels mild anxiety, a level at which, even if he did not have his new coping methods, he could still manage.

Staying in the situation

This brings us to a fundamental point. It is very important not to bite off more than we can chew: we must try to gauge how ready we are for any particular level so as to prevent avoidance. It is important from now on that the client does not run from anxiety-producing situations but *stays* in them until his anxiety has subsided. This may take a little while even using his new coping methods but *it will happen* — within 20 minutes. By ensuring that he calms down and feels relief *within* the anxiety-producing situation he will be reinforcing, and therefore building a new association between the situation and the feeling of calmness and confidence, even enjoyment. At the same time, by not gaining a sense of relief through running out or avoiding the situation, he will be starting to extinguish the association between avoidance and relief. In this way he will be reversing the way he was reinforcing his behaviour during the time that he originally built up the anxiety associations.

Sometimes other people may want the client to get into a situation which, at his current level within the programme, produces too much anxiety for him. It may be appropriate to try to resist their requests. (Chapter 6, Part 1 offers help with assertiveness.)

If the client does misjudge the level of anxiety of a situation and it is worse than he thought, he should still try to stay in it until he has calmed down a little. If he does run out, he may set himself back a little, but not all the way back to the beginning, because he may feel a little disappointed at having reverted to his old habit of rewarding himself by avoiding anxiety. He should not despair, but get back onto the staircase quickly.

Polishing the staircase

What this means is that, as he makes his way down the staircase, the client is likely to discover that he has made some steps a little too deep and others too shallow; that is, the progression downwards may be too steep and difficult, or too flat and easy. So he must alter it, adding or taking away treads, or altering the measurements of the treads *as he goes along*. Altering the levels and their parameters in this way will make it much more easy to progress smoothly and this, of course, is why we suggested that the staircase be filled in in pencil.

Going slowly and standing still

It is important for the client to *cope repeatedly* with a particular level of anxiety-producing situation until he feels confident about it, before moving down the staircase to the next level of difficulty. He will know it is definitely time to move on when the situation that used to cause anxiety now makes him feel bored!

Using the staircase every day

The client should try to enter his current level of anxiety-producing situation at least once a day. Just as with the anxiety management techniques, regular practice makes it very much easier. It is preferable to plan when in the day he will be entering his anxiety-producing situation, so that he can control that much better the parameters of where, when, who, what and how long. If, however, he finds that it is very much easier for him to act on the spur of the moment in order to prevent anticipatory anxiety building up, this is fine, he can do it that way, as long as he does not mess up the parameters of the particular level that he is on. He should try to get back to a more systematic approach as soon as he can.

Rewarding ourselves

Whenever the client goes into an anxiety-producing situation as part of his anxiety management programme, he should make sure that, while he is still in the situation, he rewards himself. This reward may be anything from a congratulatory self-statement to a treat. This reward further reinforces the new association between the situation and the feelings of pleasure and enjoyment, which will make it easier to enter the situation again or, if he is ready, to progress down the staircase. When he has decided what his rewards are going to be, he can write them down in the space at the bottom of the staircase.

Staircase summary

1 Do have as many treads as possible on your staircase.
2 Do make them as close together as possible.
3 Do define the dimensions of each tread (parameters of each level) as precisely as possible.
4 Do stay on each tread (repeatedly enter at that level) until you are completely at ease before moving on to the next.
5 Do not bite off more than you reasonably think you can chew.
6 Do not avoid or run away. Stay, use your new coping strategy and wait for the anxiety to subside.
7 Do practise every day.
8 Do reward yourself *in* anxiety-producing situations.

My personal staircase

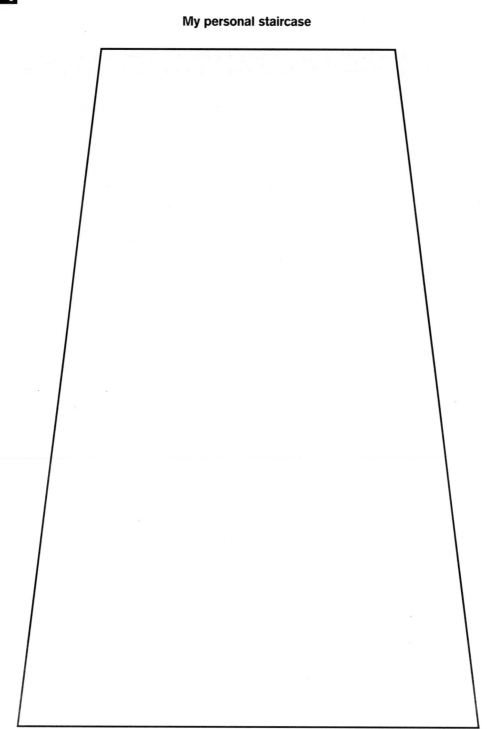

Your Anxiety Management Programme

Stage 1	Stage 2	Stage 3	Stage 4	Stage 5	Stage 6	Stage 7	Stage 8
Deep Relaxation							
		Cue Word Abdominal Breathing					
			Develop Relaxing and Competent Images				
				Develop Positive Self-Statements			
					Start Building Staircase Use Relaxing and Competent Images		
						Use Positive Self-Statements	
							START DOWN STAIR-CASE

Gloom, Sadness & Depression

You do not have to be actually feeling depressed to benefit from this chapter. It contains information, ideas and methods which can help anyone gain more control in their lives and help to prevent the thoughts and actions that lead to periods of low energy and depression.

Of all the difficulties we encounter during our lives, depression can seem the most formidable. We feel unable to act on our better instincts, to make the right choices, to do anything which makes a real difference — that is the nature of the beast. It would be unrealistic to promise that, one magical morning, a depressed individual will wake up with a song in his heart. But, however gloomy a person may feel, there are certain things they can do which will help.

In what follows we will approach depression in a way which will provide some control in coping with it. (*NB* Check Chapter 3, 'Coping'.) The client will be gently led through a framework of ideas from which he can make small but significant steps towards feeling better.

Part 1 will put feelings of depression into a context. The client will be enabled to assess his mood and identify key factors which influence the way he feels.

Part 2 will help him break through the inertia, inactivity and feelings of flatness that depression engenders.

Part 3 will help him to challenge the negative, self-destructive types of thinking that cause depression, and replace them with realistic and constructive patterns of thought.

Understanding How & Why

The beast

The first thing to understand about depression is that it is not a disease, a punishment for guilt or a sign of being crazy. It is an *experience*. It is a reaction to the world; it is the way we think, feel and act.

Everyone has times when they feel down, sad, empty, low, pessimistic, hopeless and so on. All of us feel this way at some time; it is the *degree* to which we suffer that characterizes depression.

● Depression is more intense than sadness.

● Depression lasts longer.

● Depression interferes with the way we lead our daily lives.

There are many symptoms associated with depression. The most common of these include:

● Feeling empty and/or numbed.

● Waking too early in the morning.

● Loss of energy and motivation.

● Loss of appetite.

● Sulking, self-pity, loss of confidence and self-respect.

● Poor concentration.

● Feeling distant from others.

● Feeling defeated and hopeless about oneself, the world, the future.

● Feeling that nothing we do can make any difference.

Furthermore, depression is often *passive*. It seems to just happen. It descends on us from nowhere and with no obvious explanation. This is a different experience from grief, sorrow or sadness, which may be an *active* and indeed appropriate response to a painful life event. Grief, for example, only becomes depression if the period of sorrow is extremely intense and prolonged.

How?

We have already seen in Chapter 3 how our thoughts, feelings and actions are interrelated. We have also studied the notion of reinforcement in Chapter 3. It would be helpful at this point to review that material.

It is important to try to dissolve the mystique which surrounds depression. We work on the premise that everyone can learn more about themselves and that understanding coupled with a battery of coping tactics can help anyone lead more effective and fulfilling lives. To help learn 'how we tick' it is helpful to:

- Practise self-observation: we need to record carefully exactly what is happening — what is going well, what is going wrong.
- Set realistic goals: setting targets towards which we work slowly but surely has been shown to be an effective way to introduce change into our lives (Chapter 2, Part 2).
- Reward our gains: depressed people invariably minimize or ignore their strengths and maximize their shortcomings.

Assessing mood

Everyone's mood changes from day to day. It also fluctuates throughout the day. Unfortunately, depression seems to pervade everything, making it seem that nothing can make us feel better. This exercise will help the client to be more objective about his mood. Ask him to fill in the Mood/Activities Chart once the following instructions have been read.

Instructions

This chart needs to be completed for a minimum of one week. For each day write down *what* you were doing and *how* you were feeling. Score how you felt on a scale of nought — the worst you have ever felt — to nine — the best you have ever felt. (This may be difficult to remember, but there have been times…)

At the end of the first day calculate the average score. Then mark any score above this. What is causing this slight increase in enjoyment? Is it the result of pleasure? Is it the result of achievement? Pleasure (P) is when anything nice happens to you or you do something nice. Achievement (A) is when you accomplish something and feel satisfied.

Put P or A after each rating that is higher than your average. At the end of the week add up your Ps and As. You will probably have a few and you will probably have more As than Ps.

Mood/Activities Chart

Time	Monday	Tuesday	Wednesday	Thursday	Friday	Saturday	Sunday
8.00							
9.00							
10.00							
11.00							
12.00							
13.00							
14.00							
15.00							
16.00							
17.00							
18.00							
19.00							
20.00							
21.00							
22.00							
23.00							
TOTAL P/A							

NB Try to be objective. There is no value in being as gloomy as possible about yourself: having worked this far is proof that you are trying. Convincing yourself that you are hopeless is very unhelpful.

It will also be useful to highlight any event or incident which clients think might exert a particular negative influence on their mood, such as onset of menstruation, or feeling unwanted in a group of friends or colleagues. They should keep the completed mood/activities chart safe, as it will be referred to again later on.

Depression is too complex for us to be able to pinpoint a few standard causes. In some cases it is a reaction to a very painful experience which occurred early in life; this experience becomes buried or repressed, yet exerts a hidden influence on the present. *Unlocking past conflicts can be a tortuous affair and we recommend expert professional help if any client feels the need to confront this type of problem.*

The usual cause of depression is an accumulated catalogue of minor losses, privation, self-denial, poor self-expression, high standards and feeling 'stuck' or a victim of circumstance. In such cases the actual depression is triggered by a crisis.

Always in depression we have the feeling of not living up to our standards. These standards are characterized by such words as 'ought', 'should' or 'must'. We erect high fences to jump over and if, by some supreme effort, we manage to clear a fence, we  belittle our effort — we say our standards must have been too low *because* we were successful. Our reaction is to raise the fence higher, as in show jumping competitions, to a new impossible level.

Never allowing ourselves to succeed at anything reinforces the negative image that we are not up to it. No doubt clients can think of their own examples of this.

One way to understand how a person becomes depressed is to analyse the way in which we all interrelate. The things we do can be looked at in terms of their antecedents and their consequences.

- We feel sad after visiting a relative's grave in the cemetery.

- We feel angry when we see someone dropping waste paper in the street.

- We feel happy after we have attended our yoga class.

The above examples illustrate how certain events, people and situations (antecedents) influence the way we feel. Similarly, the consequences of behaving in a certain way affect our future behaviour. For example, if our partner compliments us for cleaning the car, we feel good and are more likely to clean it the next time it is dirty. (See also *reinforcement*, pages 68–69.)

A word of warning: reward is a complex phenomenon. If depression excuses us from an unpleasant interview, for example, then we are being rewarded by our depression! This explains how some people become stuck because they fail to acknowledge the 'dividends' of being sick: it helps them avoid things they do not like. This is known as secondary gain.

For anything we might do there are three possible consequences: a positive response, a neutral response and a negative response. A neutral response is something which we view as neither positive nor negative. The difference between the eventual effects of positive and negative responses is profound.

AN EVENT	
POSITIVE RESPONSE	NEGATIVE RESPONSE
(for example, to a compliment)	(for example, to a criticism)
Feel worthwhile, wanted, respected.	Feel unwanted, unappreciated.
Do more, seek social contact.	Do less, avoid contact.
More active, feel better.	Less active, feel worse.
Feel worthwhile, wanted, respected.	Feel unwanted, unappreciated.

If we are depressed, we become increasingly involved in negative consequences:

● We become pessimistic.

● We no longer *expect* positive outcomes.

● We lose interest — why bother?

● We feel ill — there must be a reason why we feel so low.

● We think that we are letting others down.

● We brood about our guilt.

Depressed people ignore positive consequences and feel dejected by too many negative consequences of what they do. It is possible to cut through negativity by increasing our rewards and decreasing bad experiences. However, it is crucial to choose 'healthy' rewards. We might feel better after telling someone about our depression; that is, we reward ourselves by being depressed: this can encourage us to stay depressed. The client should make a list of what he considers to be negative influences on his life, such as being housebound.

Vicious and benign circles

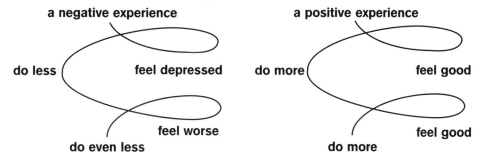

Reducing negative experiences and increasing positive experiences is a key factor in feeling less depressed.

Summary

In this part we have taken stock of the problem.

- When do we become depressed?
- What lessens the feeling of depression?
- How we can become stuck in depression by rewarding the wrong behaviour.
- How do negative beliefs outweigh any amount of positive actions?

Resolving this problem will not be easy, but becoming more objective about our experience will prepare us for the strategies outlined in Parts 2 and 3.

Review

Remind clients of the objectives listed at the beginning of this part. Have they fully *understood* and *acted upon* these? If not, return to the relevant section before proceeding.

Working with What We Do

Objectives

1 To incorporate relaxation into our daily lives.

2 To review what activities make us feel good.

3 To examine and remove blocks to a self-change plan.

4 To make a specific action plan.

Introduction

As we have seen in Part 1, people with depression can easily be defeated by a vicious circle. We feel bad so we do less, which makes us feel worse. Furthermore, we cannot do anything because our minds are too cluttered with negative thoughts about ourselves and other people.

It is debatable whether it is better to begin working on what we do or on what we think. The authors have decided to start with what we do because mobilizing ourselves will raise our energy levels so that we will quickly feel a little better about ourselves. It is important that we do not become defeated by the uphill nature of the task at this stage. Some people never get started because it seems they have too much to take on and then they become despondent that things have stayed much the same.

This part will help the client slowly and systematically to break out of the 'bad habits' which depression generates.

Relaxation

Relaxation has been emphasized as a key component of self-change throughout this book. Relaxation has benefits for the whole person:

- The body works more efficiently, for example with reduced heart rate and oxygen consumption.
- Unnecessary tensions in our daily lives can be reduced.
- We can think more clearly and solve problems more efficiently.
- We feel calmer and more at ease with our surroundings.

Relaxation is of particular importance for people prone to depression.

Many people suffering from problems associated with depression:

- feel muscular tensions, particularly in the neck and shoulders;
- feel tired, listless, enervated;
- suffer from headaches;
- have sleeping problems;
- feel tension in the gastro-intestinal region;
- become nervy or anxious, without any apparent cause.

If our bodies are stiff with tension then our muscles are using valuable energy to maintain that tautness. Learning to relax helps us to redistribute our energy to where we really need it — our brains.

Exercise

Record in the grid below the times when you feel the *most* relaxed and the *least* relaxed. In the third column, write in suggestions for helping to introduce more relaxation into your life.

Situations in which I am most relaxed	Situations in which I am least relaxed	Methods of relaxation I could use more
Playing badminton	Family mealtime	Abdominal breathing Swimming

© M Simmons & P Daw, 1994. This exercise may be photocopied for instructional use only.

The client then examines the data he has recorded:

- Can he increase the number of occasions in column 1?
- Can he practise any of the methods in column 3?
- Can he use the methods in column 1 or 3 to deal with those situations in column 2?

Case History

Bill always gets a 'tension headache' mid-afternoon at the office. He knows that this has to do with the volume of work he needs to get through, that he has a critical boss and things are not going well at home. Bill recognizes there are certain changes he needs to make in his life — his job, his relationships at home — but, *as a start*, he is going to help himself actually feel better. Walking was one of the activities he listed in column 1 so Bill is going to make a point of having a walk *every* lunch hour. Abdominal breathing was a method he listed in column 3 so he is going to practise abdominal breathing at key points in the day. In particular he plans to use abdominal breathing when he sees his boss. Getting himself into a stew about what others think of him is very unhelpful for Bill and the abdominal breathing helps him to feel noticeably calmer and more able to deal with people.

Now the client can write out a programme which will help him to consciously introduce more relaxation into his daily life.

If relaxation is sustained over a period of time it will pay dividends in the client's self-help programme. Relaxation is a specific *skill* which we learn to use in situations we perceive as threatening. It is therefore important to attain a degree of mastery in that skill so that we can instantly call on it in times of need. For example, if abdominal breathing relaxes us quickly and supermarkets make us tense, then we need to be as able to relax using our breathing techniques in the supermarket as we would in the safety and comfort of our own home.

It would be helpful at this stage to review the material in Chapters 1 and 2.

Feeling good

When engaged in activities we enjoy, we feel good. Depressed people feel little enjoyment in many things and as a result become involved in fewer and fewer pleasurable activities.

PUTTING THE HORSE BEFORE THE CART

Depressed people tend to put the cart before the horse. In this analogy the horse is our capacity for pleasure, energy and natural living. The cart is our burden of shoulds, oughts, musts and over-high standards that accompany them.

Clearly it is easier to pull than to push 'the cart'. In depression, though, we may tend to try even harder to achieve the tasks and standards we have set ourselves before we allow ourselves any pleasure. Without the opportunity to satisfy our natural needs, life becomes a dreary drudge.

To help combat feelings of depression it is necessary to take better care of ourselves and put pleasure *before* business.

Exercise

Review your Mood/Activities Chart from Part 1 of this chapter. Can you introduce more Ps into your day? Can you reorganize some of your day so your Ps precede your As? Now do the Mood/Activities Chart for a further week, this time trying to introduce more Ps and doing them earlier in the day.

- Identifying positive influences in your life will help you to be more objective about the quality of your life.
- Differentiating positive from negative experiences will help break the notion that *everything* is unsatisfying.
- You can use the Ps as a carrot to help you accomplish things you would rather avoid.
- There is a correlation between mood and engaging in pleasurable pursuits — doing nice things makes us feel better.

Make an inventory of 20 things you derive pleasure from. You might feel stuck with thoughts like "I do not seem to enjoy much these days", but try not to get bogged down by merely defining depression. There will be some activities you prefer. Use your imagination and include anything, however small, such as stroking the cat or watering the houseplants.

What is standing in the way?

- Too many 'shoulds' and 'oughts' against too few 'wants' and 'likes'. Try to obtain a balance between the jobs which must be done, such as the laundry, and things you prefer to do.

- Denying time for self. Busy people can spend their entire lives being busy and 'relaxing' by doing things that they do not really enjoy. Systematically *planning* times of pleasure, times for yourself, will help in this instance.

- Change in life style. If your main source of pleasure has been denied to you (perhaps a sporting injury prevents you running) develop alternatives.

- Feeling unwanted, uncomfortable, anxious. Are you doing what you really want, or are you trying to fulfil someone else's expectation for you? Revise material on relaxation and see Chapter 6 on assertiveness.

Write in a grid reasons why your life does not contain sufficient pleasure. Alongside record the potential remedies. For example:

What is standing in the way?	Potential remedies
Overrun by work and domestic duties	*1 Join yoga classes Thursday evenings* *2 Discuss with partner sharing workload*

Choosing activities

Remind the client of the material on goal planning. A goal should have three attributes: (a) a clear statement of *what* we want to achieve, (2) a clear statement of *how* we are going to achieve it, and (3) a clear statement of *how long* we will give ourselves to achieve it. In cases where people have become very inactive it is best to make a careful, specific plan of activities for the week. This bypasses indecision, procrastination and giving up.

How extensively this Chosen Activities Chart is filled in will vary from individual to individual, but in all cases the following points should be remembered:

- The chosen activities must be achievable and realistic. If we set ourselves up to fail by reaching too high too quickly we will keep ourselves locked in the vicious circle of feel bad — do less — feel worse.
- We should build in pleasurable activities, both for their own sake and as a carrot to help us through the chores.

Chosen Activities Chart

Time	Monday	Tuesday	Wednesday	Thursday	Friday	Saturday	Sunday
8.00							
9.00							
10.00							
11.00							
12.00							
13.00							
14.00							
15.00							
16.00							
17.00							
18.00							
19.00							
20.00							
21.00							
22.00							
23.00							

● It is not a rigid, unchangeable block, so there is no need to say "If only I didn't have to stick to a timetable I would be able to …" We can be flexible, review how we are getting on, switch things around, but give the plan a chance to have an impact on our life.

It is more important to sustain a little progress, to incorporate change into our lives regularly, than to make huge 'flash in the pan' gestures which fall flat as soon as the initial burst of energy is expended. We must try not to be blocked by our depression, but plod on.

When completing the Chosen Activities Chart, we must remember to 'put the horse before the cart'. Not only do we put pleasure before business, but we reward ourselves generously for our accomplishments.

Summary

In this part the client has been asked to scrutinize what he does in his life. Certain patterns of life contribute to depression as much as certain negative attitudes. By using skills learned in earlier chapters, the client can plan to do some things differently, which will fit his mood. Once these skills have been mobilized, he will find it easier to start working on his thoughts and beliefs, in Part 3, below.

Review

Remind clients of the objectives listed at the beginning of this part. Have they fully *understood* and *acted upon* these? If not, return to the relevant section before proceeding.

Working with Thoughts

Objectives

1 To identify positive and negative thoughts in a daily routine.

2 To practise reducing negative thoughts.

3 To increase the frequency of positive thoughts.

4 To work on inner dialogue as a means to feeling good.

Introduction

The philosopher Epictetus summed up the rationale of this part of the present chapter when he said, "Men are disturbed not by things but by the views which they take of them." In other words, it is not an event which makes us feel bad but our belief about that event. Furthermore, events never *make* us feel bad, as is commonly expressed, rather we *choose* to feel bad about them.

When our beliefs and interpretations become fixed in a negative way, we see ourselves as worthless, everything as awful and life as pointless. Fortunately, it is possible to change our beliefs. To do this we must first accept that we need *honestly* to reappraise the way we see and think about the world. Then we must challenge negative assumptions and slowly replace them with new and more positive alternatives.

Assessment

Chapter 3 explained how thoughts can influence feelings. For example, when our minds are full of the thought that we have no patience with the children, sure enough, we feel irritable and tense when the children are around.

Changing the balance of positive and negative thoughts about ourselves, others and the world is one key to freeing ourselves from the depressive mode of thinking. To do this we need to identify just what sort of thoughts we regularly entertain. Examples of positive thoughts are:

- I find that interesting.
- I'm looking forward to …

- I feel good about …
- I often laugh when …

There is no limit for positive thoughts. Some people cherish spiritual freedom and have thoughts such as:

- I feel at peace here.
- I am at one with my creator.
- I am free to love and be loved.

At this point the client should be asked to list up to 12 of his own positive thoughts. He could take up to a week to do this, identifying at least half a dozen of the most common ones. If he manages to write down 12 by the end of the week he will have done well.

People do not usually have much trouble in identifying their negative thoughts! Examples of these include:

- I'll never meet anyone I like in this town.
- My parents always put me down.
- It's all my fault that …

This time the client compiles an inventory of negative thoughts, dividing these into three categories as shown in the grid below.

NEGATIVE THOUGHTS		
ABOUT MYSELF	ABOUT OTHERS	ABOUT THE WORLD
It's my fault, I'm too selfish	*My parents always criticize me*	*I'll never meet anyone I like in this town*

© M Simmons & P Daw, 1994. This chart may be photocopied for instructional use only.

Now the ratio of positive to negative thoughts can be assessed. The idea behind actually identifying these thoughts is to help decrease the negative thoughts and increase the positive ones.

Positive thoughts

It will be recalled from the material on reinforcement (see pages 68–69) that rewarding a response makes it more likely that such a response will occur again in the future. Rewarding our positive thoughts helps nourish and sustain those thoughts:

- At least I am trying.
- I'm attempting to be positive here.
- It's a step in the right direction to …

It is most important to compliment ourselves consciously on our achievements, however small. Depressed people minimize their strengths and achievements ("That was nothing — anyone could do that"; "If I could do that, it must have been nothing") and maximize their shortcomings ("That's typical of me to mess that up"; "That just goes to show…"). We must give ourselves credit ("I remained calm with the kids at breakfast"; "I found time to ask after a friend's poorly relative"; "I cooked a tasty supper").

Prompting ourselves with positive thoughts will also help us to introduce them more regularly into our working day. Clients could carry a list of positive thoughts and refer to them at key times. They could try to associate certain actions with positive thoughts: if there is something they do several times a day, such as drink a cup of coffee, they could use this action to remind them of a positive thought.

Lastly, we should remind ourselves that depression is not a permanent condition ("I will not be like this forever"; "I am trying to break out"; "I want to feel better than this").

Negative thoughts

Part 1 of this chapter looked at the way antecedents and consequences influence our mood. Are there certain situations when we are more likely to have negative thoughts? If so, can we avoid or change those situations? Can we realistically cope in a different way? Furthermore, do we reinforce our negative thoughts? Do we use feeling low as a means of avoiding things we do not want to do? We introduced the idea of secondary gain on page 112.

Pay-offs, or secondary gains

1 "I'm hard done by." If we feel hard done by, we are trying to attract pity; we think that we ought to be helped, that 'something must be done'.
2 "I can avoid things." "I'm far too ill/depressed/anxious to do this today." In other words, someone else will have to do it for me.
3 "I am not responsible for how I feel" means I am like this because of my parents, my past rejections, my lack of opportunities.

The above ways of thinking provide rewards for being depressed. We need to identify times when we are using our symptoms as an escape because we are not helping ourselves to feel more in control.

Three techniques which can help to reduce negative thoughts are *stop*, *programmed worry* and *perspective*. Each of these techniques will contribute to reducing negative thoughts if we try them *consistently* over a long period. It is important not to give up after a couple of days if we do not notice any difference: we must keep plugging away, then record on our positive thoughts list, "I am not giving up."

Stop

Stop helps us to interrupt ourselves in midstream. Just as we are immersing ourselves in a tide of negative thoughts, we say to ourselves, or — if alone — out loud: "I am not going to think that now." We must say it and *mean* it.

Programmed worry

Some thoughts simply will not go away: we cannot forget certain events or how we behaved in a particular situation. In these cases we must allow ourselves some time each day when we can mull over these thoughts. The advantages of this technique are that we can stop constantly fretting over a problem, yet also give that problem the time and attention we feel that it deserves.

If we find these thoughts surfacing outside our 'programmed worry' we should say to ourselves (out loud if necessary) that we will only give them our attention for a specified number of minutes at a particular time.

Perspective

We have seen how depressed people tend to see many things as awful. (See page 47.) What exactly are the 'awful' consequences of doing something? The perspective technique asks the client to think about the situation which worries him and blow it up so much that it becomes more absurd than awful.

For example, he is worried about the disruption of having his boiler replaced. He imagines the worst. The boiler contractor arrives weeks late, disconnects the water, steals the client's valuables, disappears; the replacement contractor is also unreliable: he tells all the neighbours how the client has mismanaged his plumbing and his security; the client receives a bill for four times the estimate, the new boiler blows up, the house burns down and the insurance payments are overdue!

Is having a boiler replaced really that awful?

Imagery

We discussed in Chapter 3, Part 1 how thoughts have a powerful influence on feelings. Creating a visual image of a disaster (either real or imagined) can release strong negative feelings which in turn can inhibit behaviour. In the example above, visualizing the 'awful' catalogue of events could prevent us even having our boiler looked at. We feel so bad we avoid the situation. However, the process works the other way round too. Concentrating on a positive image releases positive feelings. (See also Chapter 4, 'Relaxing Image' and 'Competent Image'.)

A particularly effective technique is to use *time projection*. To do this we concentrate on how good it will be when the task is finished. Looking forward to the rewards of completing something can actually help us get started.

Another use of time projection is as a technique to help gain a perspective on problems. Simply put, this technique challenges our immediate evaluations by getting us to stand back from the present. We throw our minds *back* to some past trauma, an event which, at the time, seemed 'awful' or catastrophic. By now, however, its significance will have been greatly reduced. The passage of time leads to a less extreme valuation.

Perceiving the present as worse than it actually is does not make for an easy mind. With time projection we try to stand back from such perception; will something that today seems like the end of the world be quite that bad in the future? Projecting ourselves *forward* in time will help us to fight against negative perceptions that make us feel worse than we really need to.

Self-talk

Psychologists have suggested that we go through each day of our lives with a non-stop inner dialogue. We are not always conscious of everything we say to ourselves but in every situation that arises we assess its potential threat to our well-being, then evaluate how to cope. Some messages we give ourselves are positive:

- I'm good at this.
- Here's my chance to do well.

Some messages we give ourselves are negative:

- I'm bound to make a mess of this.
- I'll never cope.

The consequences of these messages are that giving ourselves a positive message helps us feel good and giving ourselves negative messages contributes to depression. We can therefore feel better about something by working to change our thoughts about that thing, rather than simply do something different.

Example We consider attempting to put up some shelves. It is not the job itself that worries us but our belief about our ability to do it to our satisfaction:

- I'm no good at this sort of job.
- People will look at them and will think they were botched.
- They will probably fall down.

In this case it would be more helpful to examine in more detail our beliefs than to blame our lack of skills and avoid the task.

Exercise

Think of an activity which you consider to be unpleasant, such as decorating the house. Think of all those things you say to yourself when you come to that event:

- I'm hopeless at this.
- I'm bound to make a bodge of this.
- I'll never get this done in time.
- Mark would do this much better than me.
- It's got to be done today.

Now list your examples of 'self talk' for your chosen event. Are these statements positive or negative? (In the example they were all negative.) Examine your list: do the statements seem rational or irrational?

Now pick one or two of your statements and adjust the message: remember, it is realistic to be adequate, it is self-defeating to seek perfection. Consider the following examples:

I'm bound to make a bodge of this.
I might not be a professional decorator but I will try this.
It's got to be done today.
I'd like to get this finished, but if I don't it's just unfortunate.

Dispute and adjust your own negative examples. Some tips to help you:

- Do you use the words *should* or *ought*? Can you replace them with want, prefer, like or try?

- If you *should* do something, what are the consequences of it not turning out as you wished? (See 'Perspective', page 125.)

- Do you use the words *awful, terrible, dreadful, horrible*? Can you replace them with something less extreme? It might be better if something turned out differently, but is it really awful? Why is it awful? Describe the awfulness.

- Do you use words like *always* or *never*? Can you replace these words with often, scarcely ever, sometimes or occasionally? If something has not worked out for you, is this evidence that things *never* will, that things will *always* go wrong? Can you think of any example when this has not been the case?

Negative self-talk is a way of sabotaging yourself. It is also a way of feeling worse about yourself.

- Identify activities or events which seem to precipitate bad feelings.
- Record your self-talk.
- Adjust that self-talk.
- Visualize doing the activities with new positive self-talk.
- Implement the events with positive self-talk.

I have identified these events as important for me to feel differently about:

1 ....

2 ....

3 ....

4 ....

I will use these positive self-talk messages:

1 ....

2 ....

3 ....

4 ....

Over the top

While nobody likes to be criticized, for a depressed person it can seem catastrophic. Depressed people recoil at:

- criticism or disapproval,
- not being properly appreciated,
- having things turn out differently than they had expected.

Such situations are damaging to us all, but more so for those with a *rigid* belief system. (See also Chapter 2, Parts 1 and 3; Chapter 3, Part 3.) A rigid belief system very quickly translates any criticism from others as *proof* that we are worthless, useless and hopeless. If we go over the top if somebody criticizes us we should seek the reasons why.

- Must we be perfect all of the time?
- Can we dispute rigid beliefs we hold about ourselves?
- Can we visualize being more relaxed about criticism?

Exercise

Write examples of rigid thinking that bring you unhappiness, such as 'I'll get angry if the train is late.'

1 ....

2 ....

Now write ways in which you can change such thinking: for example, 'If the train is late I can read my newspaper; the world won't come to an end.'

1 ....

2 ....

© *M Simmons & P Daw, 1994. This exercise may be photocopied for instructional use only.*

In addition to these negative thoughts which are easy to identify, we discussed negative *automatic* thoughts in Chapter 2, Part 1. These thoughts are faster and more fleeting and may exert their effects upon our emotions without our being aware of them. In fact it is partly because we do not notice them that they are so effective in making us feel bad. If we did notice them, we would see just how illogical and unfounded they are. At this point, 'Redefining the Stressor' (Chapter 2, Part 1) should be read again.

Negative automatic thoughts

Negative automatic thoughts ('NATS') have recently been identified as the main source of unpleasant emotions. As we have said before, it is often difficult to notice them because they occur very quickly. There are three ways to deal with them:

- We could keep up such an active stream of thought that there is no left-over thinking capacity for them, eg. frantic advanced mental arithmetic.

- Through meditation (see Chapter 6, Part 3): we could still our mind and reduce the amount of automatic thinking.

- We could learn to notice, identify and challenge them.

In practice the first method is not feasible — we just cannot keep up that level of mental activity. It is probably not desirable either, as it does not really confront the issue and would itself cause stress. It is best to start with the third. Once we have achieved some success in this, meditation may be very useful in helping to maintain our peace of mind.

Exercise

Make some copies of notes and the form below — Daily Record of Negative Automatic Thoughts. The client will need a few copies because he is going to carry this form and a pen with him wherever he goes and fill it in whenever he feels bad. He should look at the form carefully:

1 **Date**   Self-explanatory. It is important because you can look back and see how you are improving your ability to deal with NATS.

2 **Situation**   This can be an event that takes place externally or internally; for example, it could be a memory or a stomach ache or something someone else says.

3 **Emotion(s)**   In this column, try to identify the emotion and also rate its intensity on a scale from 0 to 100, where 0 is no emotion and 100 is the most intense imaginable.

4 **Behaviour(s)**   In this column, specify what you did as a consequence of your NATS and your emotions.

5 **NATS**   In this column, try to write down the NAT in the same words as you think it. This is a difficult task, and needs perseverance. Because NATS are so swift, it is difficult to catch them and get them down on paper. But remember, it does not have to be perfect. Just try to get something down — as you practise you will get better at it. In this column we also rate how much we believe the NAT (from 0 to 100 per cent) and then, again, how much we believe the NAT after we have analysed it and produced a rational response to it.

6 **Rational responses**   Find evidence in support of the NATS. Is there any? There is probably less than you thought. Is their case weakened as a result? Try and find evidence against the NATS — facts about what you have done and what people have said about you, for example,

Daily Record of Negative Automatic Thoughts

DATE	SITUATION Event, memory, attempt to do something	EMOTION(S) Rate intensity 0–100, before and after responses	BEHAVIOUR(S)	NATS Rate degree of belief 0–100, before and after responses	RESPONSES Rate degree of belief 0–100	TYPE OF NAT
30/6/94	Consider putting up shelf.	Despondency Hopelessness before responses: $\frac{80}{30}$ after responses:	Go to bed.	I'm useless at DIY. before response: $\frac{75}{40}$ after response:	I fixed the cupboard door. It doesn't have to be perfect. I can take it in stages. Get a DIY book. 90	Overgeneralization

that further undermine the NATS. Rate your belief in your responses from 0 to 100 per cent. Further hints for producing a rational response are included in the following questions:

- What opportunity have you had?
- Is the goal really achievable? By anyone?
- How many other people do you know who would think this?
- How do others behave towards you in different situations?
- Is the event interpreted correctly?
- Are there other ways of interpreting the event?
- How would a friend interpret the event?
- Is it really always like this? Or never?
- Is it really that bad?
- Where is the evidence?

7 **Type of NAT**   In this column, identify the type of NAT it is from the list of cognitive distortions that were discussed in detail in Chapter 2, Part 1 and which are listed below. This aspect of the exercise will enable you to become more skilled in classifying these thoughts.

Emotional reasoning	Minimizing
Overgeneralization	Selective negative focus
All-or-nothing thinking	Arbitrary inference
Magnifying	Predicting the future

Summary

In this part we have identified several techniques for challenging negative thoughts and beliefs. It is important first to actually identify automatic thoughts we have about a given situation. Behind these automatic thoughts are beliefs which can be challenged.

As well as influencing how we perceive things, our beliefs can make us hypersensitive to criticisms from others. Accepting criticism is a skill. Being able to accept criticism indicates an ability to be objective about oneself. We will return to this in Chapter 6, Part 1, 'Communicating Clearly'.

Review

Remind clients of the objectives listed at the beginning of this part. Have they fully *understood* and *acted upon* these? If not, return to the relevant section before proceeding.

Conclusions

In this chapter we have examined factors which cause and contribute to depression:

- how depression manifests itself;
- how what we do influences our mood;
- how to work on our thought processes.

The main problem with working constructively through depression is that it is an unpleasant experience. Most people would rather avoid confronting it. When a bout of depression passes, why sit down and stir up all those negative emotions? The answer is that putting such things out of mind is not conducive to mental health. Feeling in control of our lives involves understanding 'how we tick' mentally, emotionally and spiritually.

Depression is not permanent and can be combated. It is hoped that this chapter will have begun that process. In the next chapter we will look at healthier ways of being.

6

Growing Further

This chapter looks at ways to deal assertively with others, to understand intimate relationships and to develop our inner selves.

Part 1 concentrates on training ourselves to communicate more assertively.

Part 2 examines intimate relationships. Learning how we relate to others tells us a great deal about ourselves.

Part 3 introduces meditation as a passport to realizing more of our potential as a person. In addition there is a one-week programme to help develop positive attitudes.

Communicating Clearly

Introduction

People are social animals and in order to function effectively we therefore need to be able to communicate clearly. In this section we will practise ways to conduct direct, open and honest styles of relating to others. We will learn how to relate our own needs, wants and feelings, while respecting the same individual rights of others.

The alternative to communicating clearly is manipulation, 'saving people's feelings' (our own), becoming aggressive or passively avoiding a situation (while boiling inside). The English 'stiff upper lip' has no relevance in today's society of demand and change. Our style of communicating overtly reflects our inner values and feelings. Those greedy for power and control know that bombastically crushing others is a means to an end, but at what cost to human dignity and their self-esteem? Those who time and time again allow themselves to be exploited, put down and ignored eventually become timid, clinging in relationships, over-anxious to please and depressed.

Learning how to communicate effectively means learning more about ourselves, our values, our beliefs, our insecurities and our needs.

Assessing ourselves

The client should consider the six statements below:

1 Don't argue. If I don't want to mend the car then I won't.

2 If it's all right with you, would you mind if I possibly went home early tonight?

3 I would like to go out and eat tonight; what do you think?

4 I have thought about what you said to me yesterday but I feel that it is up to me to decide for myself.

5 I don't know if it is okay with you, but I wonder if you would mind going to the shops for me?

6 You'd better not be late again.

Can he imagine himself saying any of the above? Can he discriminate between the different styles?

Statements 1 and 6 are *aggressive*: they only express the speaker's point of view, they invite confrontation, they attempt to beat the other person into submission.

Statements 2 and 5 are *passive*: the speaker is submissive, inviting a rejection; he fails to own what he wants and to express himself clearly. Passive communicators manipulate or are manipulated.

Statements 3 and 4 are *assertive*: the speaker says clearly and confidently what he wants or feels, without in any way denying the rights of others. When acting assertively, people:

● communicate their needs clearly, openly and honestly;

● negotiate with others and compromise when appropriate;

● value their own rights and those of others;

● deal with situations in a confident and relaxed manner.

Compare this with people who manipulate or coerce others; are evasive and dishonest; will not come to the point; bottle up their feelings; or always give in or insist on their own way.

Situations requiring assertiveness skills

There are numerous situations which call for an assertive response. Several times a day we can find ourselves reflecting on our interactions with others and wondering whether we handled the situation as well as we might. Types of situation requiring an assertive response include the following:

● At work — coping with a boss, negotiating with other workers, experiencing sexual discrimination or racism.

- Organizing our social lives — refusing requests on our time, stating preferences.
- With others — paying compliments, accepting criticism, complaining.

BILL OF RIGHTS

1. *I have the right to state my own needs and set my own priorities as a person, independent of any roles that I may assume in my life.*

2. *I have the right to be treated with respect as an intelligent, capable and equal human being.*

3. *I have the right to express my feelings.*

4. *I have the right to express my opinions and values.*

5. *I have the right to say 'yes' or 'no' for myself.*

6. *I have the right to make mistakes.*

7. *I have the right to change my mind.*

8. *I have the right to say 'I don't understand'.*

9. *I have the right to ask for what I want.*

10. *I have the right to decline responsibility for other people's problems.*

11. *I have the right to deal with others without being dependent on them for approval.*

We are all responsible for our own values, but it is suggested that the above list represents what all human beings are entitled to. If anyone has problems accepting those rights for themselves and for others this indicates the need to work on becoming more assertive.

Skills

Being constructive and positive

Accepting praise and making compliments are both integral aspects of assertive behaviour. If we feel comfortable with positive dialogue this indicates good self-esteem, and vice versa. There is no need to leave our love and respect for others unexpressed. Finding it hard to accept a compliment probably indicates a negative residue from childhood which convinces us that there is something wrong with us.

Negotiating our needs

It is all too easy to take a line of least resistance. We can all think of situations when we say 'yes' when we want to say 'no', or when we feel coerced into line, or when we feel 'got at' or 'put down'. To communicate assertively it is crucial to relate our needs to someone else in a calm, rational way. It is, of course, equally important to listen to what is being said to us, to seek clarification if necessary and to empathize with the needs and rights of others.

In negotiating our needs it is therefore important to go into a situation with clear goals. We must think ahead: do we *really* want to ask our partner for time to ourselves, or do we *really* want a good row? By knowing what we really need we can plan how to express it.

If our request to someone is met with "You always...", then that person is responding to the *process* of our dialogue and not the content — *how* we are saying something as opposed to *what* we are saying. When we feel blocked or manipulated by another it is because they are reacting unassertively: that can feel very uncomfortable. "You always ..." responses usually occur in situations that are very emotionally tense, as in families. Most commonly, once one person reacts in this way, another emotional response is elicited that exacerbates the problem.

To communicate clearly with another, the golden rule is to acknowledge the *emotions* and *needs* of the other person before concentrating on the facts. Emotion is a non-rational state that needs immediate recognition. It is like an upset child: it will continue its demands until we attend to it. Therefore it is important to show we appreciate how others feel before concentrating on the facts of the situation: failure to do so will result in feelings continuing to express themselves until they are acknowledged — and that gets in the way of clear communication. The examples below illustrate how to respond to emotion and need first:

- I can see you are desperate to find a baby-sitter (*emotion + need*) but I have plans for this evening.
- You must have been so upset (*emotion*) when you didn't get that job; I know you really wanted it (*need*).

Dialogue is a two-way process and to communicate skilfully we need to be able to respond to the needs of others, as well as clearly convey our own needs.

Reflective listening: to help practise responding to the emotional content of speech we use this formula as a reply when people talk to us:

So you feel ... about ...

Remember emotions are feelings: for example, anger, sadness, happiness or frustration. Reflective listening reassures people that (1) you appreciate how they feel, and (2) you have heard their opinion/statements of fact. So when negotiating our needs we must learn to:

1 Make clear goals for ourselves before speaking.

2 Acknowledge the emotional content of the other person's speech.

3 Concentrate on the content of what we are saying.

Protecting ourselves

Other people can be quite poisonous at times! If we feel vulnerable to unrealistic requests, to being put on the spot, to being labelled or analysed, then we badly need skills in assertiveness. However, we are also our own worst enemies. Working on the inner dialogue (see Chapter 5, Part 3) is a powerful method for silencing the inner critic who demands so much from us.

Rehearsing

If only we could come up with the smart answer at the time and not when we are walking home with a sore ego. If we can identify situations when we are likely to need assertiveness skills, we should practise them beforehand.

In rehearsing approaches or responses to people, we must first identify our goals, then identify what skills we may need (such as reflective listening) and finally identify how we will present ourselves (see below). Communication, like any skill, must be mastered gradually by practising.

Self-presentation

'Body language' and 'Non-verbal behaviour' are two commonly used expressions to describe the signals we give off to people about what we are thinking and feeling. For example, if we cross our arms when talking to somebody we are probably feeling under threat and therefore need to protect ourselves.

To communicate assertively it is necessary to cultivate the following:

A relaxed posture   Assuming an open stance clearly conveys the message of being calm and being prepared to listen. Some situations, however, such as refusing to loan someone money, require a more rigid and closed posture: you are not open to negotiation, you mean 'no'.

A calm and controlled voice   Sounding decisive and controlled is compatible with being clear, open and honest. By preparing ourselves and concentrating on the tone of our voice we stand a much better chance of conveying our needs. Shouting, whining or being patronizing will only help to alienate the other.

Proximity Communication is maintained by appropriate proximity. If we come too close we invade the other's 'personal space'; if we stay too far away, this implies weakness, remoteness and lack of resolve.

Eye contact Steady eye contact indicates that we mean what we are saying. Glaring or staring should be avoided as this can be intimidating. At the other extreme, looking down at our feet or fixing our eyes on some point behind the other person can seem shifty or anxious.

'I' statements When expressing our needs, we remember that these needs belong to ourselves. Therefore we try to start sentences with 'I'. This is important because it shows that we are owning our statements. Thus we say: "I feel hot", as opposed to "it's hot in here"; "I want to go out", as opposed to "I wonder if ..." or "would you mind if ..."; or "I think that is good", as opposed to "I suppose ..." or "I guess ..." These examples may appear to be minor adjustments, but in fact, by subtly changing the way we phrase things, we create a significantly more positive impression.

One method of developing these skills is to practise them in front of a mirror at home. Some situations we know in advance will be difficult for us, so we should prepare both what we want to say and how we will say it. If we can master the basic skills we will increase our chances of performing effectively in all situations.

Further skills

The two skills which follow owe their effectiveness to the repeated restatement of needs or opinions by the assertive individual. For this reason both these skills are sometimes known as the 'Broken Record' technique: we repeat our need simply and categorically in a relaxed manner without any justification or apology until the other person meets our need or agrees to negotiate.

Repeated refusal

This is a self-protective skill. It is the exercise of the right to refuse requests without having to justify ourselves. Consider the telephone conversation below between mother and daughter:

Mother: Hello, I'm phoning to say that I'm free on Sunday and I thought it would be a good idea if I came over for a visit.

Daughter:	Oh … I've got quite a lot to do on Sunday.
Mother:	Never mind about that, I could help you.
Daughter:	The problem is that I wanted to catch up with a load of things I've been putting off.
Mother:	I won't be in the way.
Daughter:	And Simon has got a bit of a cold starting.
Mother:	Then he needs his grandmother. Shall we say late morning then?
Daughter:	Umm … right … see you Sunday then. …

In the above example, the daughter actually wanted to say 'no'. Rather than do this she made excuses and tried to be vague. By not being specific she ended up giving in. She was prepared to sacrifice her own needs and feelings for those of her mother. What she really wanted to say was, "I'm sorry, but you cannot come." That might seem a little blunt, however. To negotiate effectively the daughter must first acknowledge the *needs* and *emotions* of her mother, then concentrate on her own needs and feelings. This is the formula discussed above, in 'Negotiating our needs'. The conversation could have gone thus:

Mother:	Hello, I'm phoning to say that I'm free on Sunday and I thought it would be a good idea if I came over for a visit.
Daughter:	It would be a good idea, Mum, but unfortunately I'm not free on Sunday.
Mother:	You can't be busy all day.
Daughter:	No, but I think it better if we leave it this week.
Mother:	Its ages since I've seen the children.
Daughter:	Mum, I know you want to see the children but it's not convenient this Sunday.
Mother:	I'm going to be on my own here. Look, I promise I won't be in the way; I could take Simon out or something and that would leave you more time to get on with your work.
Daughter:	You've obviously set your heart on coming over and I know you must be feeling very disappointed, but we are not free this Sunday.
Mother:	In that case I'll have to stop in on my own.
Daughter:	While you are on the phone let's make a date when it is

	convenient for you to come over. How about lunch next Saturday?
Mother:	I would have preferred this Sunday.
Daughter:	I'm not free Sunday; how about next Saturday?
Mother:	Okay. Maybe it was a bit short notice for you. I'll see you next Saturday, then. Expect me at about 11.30.
Daughter:	We'll look forward to that. 'Bye.

Repeated refusal cuts through the cycle of *manipulation — guilt — giving in — resentment* that characterizes so many non-assertive interactions. In the above example the mother was really turning the emotional screws. However, the daughter was clear — in this instance she wanted to put her own needs first. Yes, her mother would experience some let-down — assertiveness does not claim to be a magic wand that makes all unpleasant situations disappear — but assertive behaviour helps the individual to get what is best out of the situation while remaining sensitive to the needs of others. The alternative here was for the daughter to give in to the manipulation and feel resentment and anger towards her mother. Dealing with the situation needed the daughter's short-term investment for long-term gain. If she had given in this time, her mother might feel free to come over *every* time she wished.

In some situations each party tries to make the other feel guilty and thus give in under pressure: one makes the other feel guilty about making the request, the other makes the one feel guilty about refusing it. These cycles must be broken.

Repeated request

This skill is most useful when we ask for things we believe to be rightfully ours. We need to ask repeatedly without being sidetracked into reasons or rationale. We need to keep to the point and not respond to jibes or attempts to make us feel guilty for asking for our rights.

Both the skills of repeated refusal and repeated request are used most appropriately when energy and time are at a premium. They are also handy when we anticipate being diverted from our objectives by clever but irrelevant argument. In general we should stick to the formula: first acknowledge the needs and feelings of others, then make our request.

Example: "I know you're hard up, but you promised to pay me back today and I need the money."

Exercise: practice with images

To begin with you need to identify clearly situations in which you want to be more assertive.

1 Close your eyes and imagine one of your chosen scenes. Try and conjure a detailed picture of what is going on, who else is there and so on, as if you were watching a movie.

2 When it is your moment to speak in the 'movie' repeat your lines in an assertive manner. Do not react aggressively or passively.

3 Repeat your lines until you feel comfortable with them. Have you checked posture and tone of voice? The idea is not to sound like Oscar Wilde or to triumph at another person's expense, merely to handle the situation satisfactorily.

4 Imagine how others would respond to your assertive statements. Try and visualize both a positive and a negative response — how will you cope with these? Repeat this sequence two or three times.

5 Practise this procedure for at least a week and then transfer the images to real life.

6 Remember, you are not seeking to control, coerce, put someone in their place and so on.

7 Start with easier situations, when you are more likely to succeed.

© M Simmons & P Daw, 1994. This exercise may be photocopied for instructional use only.

Summary

Our communication style reflects our inner values. Learning to be assertive:

● enables us to be true to our own needs, feelings and thoughts;

● encourages direct, open and honest interactions with others;

● improves our self-esteem.

If we can express ourselves confidently we will consequently develop more self-confidence. If we dodge tricky issues or shout until we get our own way we are undervaluing the basic human rights of ourselves and others.

Review

Remind clients of the objectives listed at the beginning of this part. Have they fully *understood* and *acted upon* these? If not, return to the relevant section before proceeding.

Relationships

Objectives

1 To assess how we handle our relationships.

2 To work towards creating equality in our partnerships.

Introduction

The subject of relationships is huge and worthy of its own book. In this small space we cannot do justice to many aspects of relationships, but we can identify key issues.

How we relate to others says a great deal about ourselves. It is by being with others that we learn about ourselves. If relationships are a source of difficulty for a client, he will benefit from taking the time to analyse why. The problems that people do experience are too numerous to list, but include the following:

1 An inability to make a commitment to another person.
2 An insatiable need for reassurance or demonstrations of affection.
3 Jealousy.
4 Sexual insecurity.
5 Picking the 'wrong' partner.

Whatever the partnership, finding and nurturing a loving relationship is one of the most joyous and meaningful human experiences. With such high stakes, the flip-side of a good relationship can be an experience of misery and despair.

Nurturing a loving relationship necessarily involves *negotiating* our own needs while trying to meet the needs of our partner. We have already learned skills that have helped us effectively

● to assess areas of difficulty,

● to understand how our life style might be contributing to the problem,

● to make an action plan to reduce our distress.

Involving a partner in this process may be a fruitful experience for both parties. Every relationship can grow by examining attitudes towards sharing, conflict, sex and intimacy.

Sharing

One essential ingredient of a fulfilling partnership is being able to share pleasant activities. This is not to say that couples need to spend all their leisure time together; in fact being comfortable with one another's independent pursuits is a good barometer of emotional maturity.

In our relationships we need to find a balance between our own needs, those of our partner and the relationship itself. Couples who spend very little time together, or who have a routine way of filling time, should benefit from exploring activities they might share.

Conflict

In every partnership there are disagreements and times of conflict. In a good relationship conflict is worked through and can be a source of mutual growth. When conflict becomes 'stuck', communication breaks down and feelings of bitterness or resentment endure. Then the relationship needs work.

In the client's relationship, can he balance his needs with his partner's? Can he compromise (see Chapter 2, Part 1)? Does he seek dominance or equality? Does he manipulate or coerce his partner or seek common solutions? Does he project unwanted aspects of his personality onto his partner (Chapter 3, Part 4)?

Usually, for reasons outlined in Chapter 3, Part 4, we choose a partner who is apparently different from us in significant ways. Our partner may manifest certain qualities that lie dormant in ourselves. Our partner may sometimes be a screen onto whom we can project our early feelings towards one of our own parents.

Psychologists have distinguished between two major types of partnership: the complementary one and the symmetrical one. Complementary relationships can be described in terms of two halves making a whole. They are typically, though not necessarily, traditional partnerships wherein the partners fulfil complementary roles which never overlap. For example, her domain is the house, his is work, the garden and garage.

A symmetrical relationship, by contrast, contains few fixed roles and those that are fixed are made so through considerations of expertise. The remainder of the roles in the partnership are open to negotiation.

Complementary Partnership	Symmetrical Partnership
One partner dominates	Equal power to both
Roles/tasks divided	Roles/tasks shared
Little room for personal growth	Much room for personal growth
Little conflict until one changes	Occasional conflict in partner negotiation
Little room for both partners to pursue individual needs	Room for individual need fulfilment
Further polarization likely	Greater harmony likely

Exercise

Consider the three main areas of domestic life outlined below:

1 **Chores**

Who shops and cooks?
Who cleans the house?
Who mends the clothes?
Who does the laundry?
Who washes up?
Who does the garden?
Who does the decorating?

2 **Children**

Who gets up in the night?
Who puts the children to bed?
Who chooses their clothes?
Who organizes birthday parties?
Who takes them to school and collects them afterwards?
Who mostly takes charge of discipline?

3 **Choices**

Who decides which holiday to take?
Who chooses the motor car?
Who chooses the house decor or furnishings?
Who manages the finances?
Who selects social or leisure pursuits?

Who goes out to work?
Whose work influences more aspects of family life?

When judging the success of a relationship, it is necessary to ask whether *both* partners experience harmony and satisfaction.

- What would be the consequences of one partner changing roles?
- Would they be able to?
- Would it be better to discuss these things together?

If one partner feels devalued and unappreciated, these feelings will sneak out and interfere with other areas of the relationship.

© *M Simmons & P Daw, 1994. This exercise may be photocopied for instructional use only.*

Sex

There is no ideal formula for frequency of sex, sexual techniques, capacity for orgasm and so on. The only guideline is whether the above are *mutually* agreed upon, or whether one partner seeks dominance and control. Thus the mature couple

- have a clear idea of their individual sexual needs and preferences;
- can communicate their needs to each other;
- respond to their partner's needs and likes;
- can ask one another for sex without fear of rejection;
- can achieve orgasm given conducive circumstances.

If we find ourselves having sexual difficulties this might be symptomatic of other personal problems, such as stress, anxiety or depression, and the relevant chapter should be worked through.

If a client cannot approach his sexuality honestly and openly he might need to consult a marriage guidance counsellor or sex therapist.

Intimacy

Intimacy within a relationship involves revealing ourselves to our partner. We should be able to disclose goals and plans; private thoughts and feelings; and fears and disappointments. Our attitudes to intimacy reflect how we feel about ourselves. We may worry about loss of control, rejection or embarrassment.

Feeling uncomfortable with intimacy is often linked to our experiences as a child. Perhaps we were not shown affection; perhaps we are hiding more painful memories.

NB Unlocking childhood traumas requires professional help and we would recommend the service of a trained psychotherapist.

Summary

In this part there has been the opportunity to examine whether we base our relationships on equality and love, or whether we rely on coercion and dominance to maintain control.

Trying to be less judgemental and critical will help us to begin the process of truly loving another for who they are, rather than for what they do for us.

Review

Remind clients of the objectives listed at the beginning of this part. Have they fully *understood* and *acted upon* these? If not, return to the relevant section before proceeding.

Meditation

Objectives

1 To learn the basic principles of meditation.

2 To practise different meditation techniques.

3 To introduce a one-week positive attitudes programme into clients' lives.

Introduction

There is no limit to the process of realizing our potential as a person and this chapter opens up ideas which engender growth. Anyone who stops growing as a person — no matter how old — is effectively stating they know all there is to know: what an extraordinary claim this is! The truth is that, when we stop allowing ourselves to grow, to find new experiences and ways of being, stagnancy is just around the corner.

Even if it is extremely difficult for us to change our circumstances, it is always possible to avoid dull sameness in our outlook on life. Perhaps the most effective way to remain open, to give room to our intuitions, to allow the flow of deeper thoughts and feelings within us, is to meditate.

Meditation

Introducing meditation into our day will, in time, have a profound influence on the quality of our lives. Practised regularly, meditation

- increases concentration;
- revitalizes mind and body;
- helps us slow down, absorb and reflect;
- allows our intuitive thoughts and feelings to surface;
- enables spiritual values to evolve.

Unfortunately, misconceptions about meditation abound:

- Will I have to sit cross-legged?
- Do I need to be religious?
- Must I travel to India to learn it?
- Isn't it voodoo, hypnotism, mumbo-jumbo?

The answer to all these questions is a resounding *no*. Meditation is not a dangerous cult pastime, it is a way of being. Meditation helps us to get in touch with the present; it involves a way of thinking that clears away all the hustle and bustle of our busy lives and chattering thoughts; it seeks to help us focus on the peace that lies within our inner selves.

One common misconception about meditation is that there is only one proper way to do it, and that we must join a (possibly expensive) class to find out how. There are numerous ways to meditate, some of which we will outline, leaving it to the client to select the one(s) which suit him best.

Basics

No matter which method is chosen, there are some basics which should be adhered to: (1) Choose a room where you will not be too distracted by other people, outside noises, interruptions and so on. (2) You will need to relax yourself before you begin, to reduce the tension in your body, to shut down bothersome thoughts. (3) You will need to find a position in which you will be comfortable for 10–20 minutes. Sitting cross-legged has postural advantages only if your knees are used to it. Otherwise use a comfortable chair or a big cushion; lying down is fine. (NB Do not sleep.) (4) Try to adopt a calm, serene attitude. You are not waiting for anything to happen, such as a light showing in your head. You are not doing, you are being here now. (5) Eyes should be closed unless the candle technique is being used.

Methods

Remember, there is no one correct way to meditate. There are countless texts that you could refer to; below we offer guidelines to a number of techniques.

Breathing   Simply be aware of your breath for 10–20 minutes. Breathe gently and evenly. Feel the air coming through your nose, feel your chest and abdomen rise and fall, allow the air to come in and out like the flow and ebb of the tide. If your thoughts wander — which they will — bring them back to slow inhalation and exhalation of breath. Do not hold your breath in or out, simply be aware of its movement.

Mantra   Some people find repeating a word over and over to themselves in rhythm with their breath a useful technique. You could choose any word of any language; for example, peace, father, gum, hymn are words that either comfort or have a reassuring resonance. Repeat your chosen word on the in breath, or the out breath, or even both. The most common word is 'om' (pronounced a-u-m) which is the Sanskrit word denoting a universal chord.

Clouds   As you sit or lie, with your breath slow and controlled, imagine your mind to be a perfect blue sky. As your thoughts arise, think of them as clouds floating across the sky. Do not hang on to your clouds, let them drift past, leaving your mind as clear as the open sky. A variation of this technique is to put your thoughts into bubbles and allow them to drift out of sight.

River   Imagine yourself sitting beside a slow-moving river. Your breathing is slow and even. The river is moving through your mind; the water is clear. As a thought emerges let it go downstream away from you. Keep sitting by the crystal-clear waters of the river.

Candle   Dim the lights in your room and set a lighted candle before you. Imagine the flame of the candle in the centre of your forehead. Imagine you are the flame and it you. Close your eyes and sustain the image of the candle in the middle of your forehead. When the image fades, open your eyes again and look at the candle. There is only the candle; do not allow any other thoughts to linger, only the clarity of the candle flame.

Love   Love is a technique used by the Buddhists and asks you to replace your 'attack' thoughts about the world and others with love. 'Go deep into your heart', the Buddhists say, and this is what is required in this instance. Become silent within and seek an area of your heart where you can feel love. Perhaps you can remember a particular person, or even a pet, for whom you feel, or have felt, great love. Cultivate that love, allowing it to spread from its source. Feel its influence moving outwards to your family and friends, your colleagues. You are embracing everyone with a love which emanates from you like waves from the centre of a lake. Allow your love to expand ever-outwards into your community, your town, your country, the world, the universe …

Yellow room   Yellow room is a perfect exercise to share with a partner. One of you can read the following script slowly to the other, with plenty of pauses, and on a later occasion you can reverse the roles.

"Sit down with your eyes closed. Relax your shoulders; breathe gently in and out, in and out without effort. Feel yourself becoming calm. Now focus your attention on a spot between the eyebrows and the hair-line in the middle of your forehead. Feel an amber glow there. Don't strain; relax, feel a source of golden light within your forehead. Now allow this light to spread outwards. You are surrounded by this golden light. Breathe easily and feel the radiance and the warmth. You are cocooned in a warm amber glow. This glow is a beautiful amber room.

"You are lying in the room, relaxed, comfortable, content, at peace. The room is warm and peaceful, flooded with golden light. If you wish you may walk around this golden room. Stand up and feel how light your body feels. You notice a window in the room which you look out of. Outside is everything you want to see. Anything you want is outside the window. From your safe cocoon you can gaze out of the window or simply return to the room, back to the warm amber room. Now focus the light onto your forehead. When you are ready, open your eyes."

That is your personal yellow room: you may enter it at any time you wish. In further meditation you may want to spend longer at the window and explore outside.

Using affirmations

We have already seen in earlier chapters how our perceptions affect our reactions to the world. Furthermore, our attitudes and values shape our perceptions and it is easy to become fixed in our attitudes and values. The advantage of becoming fixed is that it saves effort thinking about things in any depth and we know where we stand. The disadvantage is that our actions and reactions become habitual to the point where we cease to notice the flow of life around us and we feel ground down into a futile mess.

Transforming our lives is possible if we are prepared to work on our fixed attitudes and reactions. One method to do this is to carry around affirmations to remind ourselves of throughout the day. A list of such thoughts, together with a short explanation as to their usefulness, follows.

I can see things differently   There is no one way to view the world. We do not have to hang on to our perceptions like a junkie to a drug. Beyond conflict and pain lies the search for love and acceptance. We need to look at our choices. Do we only seek conflict and find fault with others?

I will give up negative thoughts about others   There is no value in carrying conflict around with us. Our negative thoughts beget other negative thoughts — the broken wheel turns on and on. Often negative thoughts are really about ourselves — others merely remind us of what is unacceptable in us. We must try to let go of hostile thoughts and actively replace them with positive thoughts. We must try to go through the day without judging anyone — how do we feel when someone judges us?

I am not a victim   Feeling trapped has negative origins in past failure, guilt or fear. Carrying around a negative attitude influences our perceptions of the present and limits our choices. We are free to start making our own choices about how we see the world and how we react to others.

There is only the present   Most of the time we feel squeezed between the guilt of our past and fear of the future. Rerunning failures and fantasizing future catastrophes is not conducive to mental health! We must stop projecting all that has happened before into the present, and see the present in its immediate *now*.

I will learn to love   It is very easy to go around pronouncing judgement on others and bolstering our own self-righteousness. It is difficult to forget old wounds and seek to forgive, to find harmony and love. From today we must approach each new situation with an open heart, leave the judge behind us and try to love our fellow beings as we would wish to be loved.

I am responsible for what I feel   How many times do we say things like "You make me feel. ...."? When we become aware of our own choices this no longer applies — we are all responsible for the way we react to others. Furthermore, it is unrealistic to wait for others to change. If we want things to be different it is up to us to sort out our corner of the universe and stop blaming everyone else for what is going wrong.

I seek peace in all things. This is self-explanatory. We leave behind our lust for conflict, blame and self-righteousness and actively seek forgiveness, love and peace.

Exercise

Transfer the seven affirmations listed above onto seven pieces of card, one for each day of the week. Read your 'thought for the day' first thing in the morning and last thing at night, contemplating its meaning for 10–15 minutes. Practised seriously, these thoughts can help to release you from the burden of the past, and free you to experience the fullness and completeness of your life *now*. Take your 'thought for the day' with you wherever you go, referring to it and putting the principles into practice at regular intervals.

Summary

Meditation can give our lives quality. It is a way of *being* which, if practised regularly, will have a beneficial influence on all areas of our lives. We do not need to sit on top of a mountain to meditate, the idea is to find the peace of the mountains within us and bring it to the busy market-place.

Review

Remind clients of the objectives listed at the beginning of this part. Have they fully *understood* and *acted upon* these? If not, return to the relevant section before proceeding.

Conclusion

There can never be an end to a book such as this. Every completed goal becomes the next point of departure. There are no limits to personal growth.

It goes without saying that merely reading relevant texts will not be sufficient to change the behaviour of those seeking help. It will be necessary to supervise closely many of the exercises, to encourage users to see through work that they have started on, and to practise regularly their newly acquired coping skills. Gains can often be painfully slow, yet once the movement to change is started it can quickly gain momentum.

We would welcome any comments either from professionals or from their clients about the effectiveness of different programmes and exercises.

Further Reading

For the user

Diagram Group, *Man's Body*, Corgi, London, 1977.

Dickson A, *A Woman in Your Own Right*, Quartet Books Ltd, London, 1982.

Dickson A, *The Mirror Within*, Quartet Books Ltd, London, 1988.

Gilbert S, *The Psychology of Dieting*, Routledge, London, 1989.

Gillett R, *Overcoming Depression*, Dorling Kindersley, London, 1991.

Hewitt J, *Teach Yourself Meditation*, Hodder & Stoughton, London, 1978.

Hewitt J, *Teach Yourself Relaxation*, Hodder & Stoughton, London, 1985.

Jampolsky GG, *Love is Letting Go of Fear*, Celestial Arts, Berkeley, California, 1979.

LeShan L, *How to Meditate: A Guide to Self-discovery*, Aquarian Press, Harper Collins, London, 1993.

Lindenfield G, *Assert Yourself*, Thorson Publishing, Wellingborough, 1986.

Litvinoff S, *The Relate Guide to Better Relationships*, Ebury Press, London, 1992.

Orbach S, *Fat is a Feminist Issue*, Hamlyn, London, 1979 and *Fat is a Feminist Issue II*, Hamlyn, London, 1982.

Postle D, *The Mind Gymnasium*, Macmillan, London, 1989.

Proto L, *Meditation for Everybody*, Penguin, Harmondsworth, 1991.

Rowe D, *Beyond Fear*, Fontana, London, 1987.

Rowe D, *Depression – The Way Out of Your Prison*, Routledge & Kegan Paul, London, 1983.

Toates F, *Obsessional Thoughts and Behaviour*, Thorson Publishing, Wellingborough, 1990.

Zilbergeld B, *Men & Sex*, Fontana, London, 1988.

For the practitioner

Barlow DH & Cerney JA, *Psychological Treatment of Panic*, Guildford Press, New York, 1988.

Beck AT, *Cognitive Therapy and the Emotional Disorders*, Penguin, London, 1989.

Beck AT & Emery G, *Anxiety Disorders and Phobias*, Basic Books, New York, 1985.

Da Silva P & Rachman S, *Obsessive Compulsive Disorder: The Facts*, Oxford University Press, Oxford, 1992.

Duker M & Slade R, *Anorexia Nervosa & Bulimia: How to Help*, Open University Press, Buckingham, 1988.

Fontana D, *Managing Stress*, Routledge BPS, London, 1989.

Gilbert S, *The Psychology of Dieting*, Routledge, London, 1989.

Holland S & Ward C, *Assertiveness: A Practical Approach*, Winslow Press Limited, Bicester, 1990.

Kennerley H, *Managing Anxiety: A Training Manual*, Oxford Medical Publications, Oxford, 1990.

Parry G, *Coping with Crises*, Routledge BPS, London, 1990.

Powell T, *The Mental Health Handbook*, Winslow Press Limited, Bicester, 1992.

Scott M, *A Cognitive Behavioural Approach to Clients' Problems*, Routledge Tavistock, London, 1989.

Emergencies: Samaritans offer advice to anyone in distress. Check the telephone directory for contact numbers.

Age Concern England
Astral House
1268 London Rd
London SW16 4ER
0181-679 8000

Alcoholics Anonymous
PO Box 1
Stonebow House
Stonebow
York YO1 2NJ
01904 644026

Association for Child Psychology & Psychiatry
St Saviours House
39–41 Union Street
London SE1 1SD
0171-403 7458

Association of Child Psychotherapists
Burgh House
New End Square
London NW3 1LT
0171-403 7458

Association of Clinical Hypnotherapists
229a Sussex Gardens
Lancaster Gate
London W2 2RL
0171-402 9037

Association for Group & Individual Psychotherapy
1 Fairbridge Rd
London N19 3EW
0171-272 7013

Association of Humanistic Practitioners
BCM AHPP
London WC1N 3XX
0181-749 6005

British Association of Counselling
1 Regent Place
Rugby CV21 2PJ
01788 578328

British Association of Psychotherapists
37 Mapesbury Road
London NW2 4HJ
0181-452 9823

Cruse – Bereavement Care
126 Sheen Road
Richmond
Surrey TW9 1UR
0181-940 4818 (administration)
Helpline: 0181-332 7227
(Mon–Fri 9.30am – 5.30pm)

Eating Disorders Association
Sackville Place
44 Magdalen Street
Norwich NR3 1JU
01603 619090

Gamblers Anonymous
PO Box 88
London SW10 0EU
0171-384 3040

Gay & Lesbian Switchboard
0171-837 7324

Gingerbread (one-parent families)
49 Wellington St
London WC2E 7BN
0171-336 8183

Human Potential Research Project
Adult Education Dept
University of Surrey
Guildford
Surrey GU2 5XH
01483 300800

London Rape Crisis Centre
PO Box 69
London WC1X 9NJ
0171-916 5466 (office line)
0171-837 1600 (counselling)

Mental Health Advice Centre
1 Southbrook Rd
London SE12 8LH
0181-318 1330

Mental Health Foundation
37 Mortimer St
London W1N 8JU
0171-580 0145

MIND
Granta House
15–19 Broadway
Stratford
London E15 4BQ
0181-519 2122

Narcotic Anonymous
PO Box 1980
London N19 3LS
0171-730 0009

NSPCC
42 Curtain Road
London EC2A 3NH
Helpline Advice
0800 800500

Phobics Society
4 Cheltenham Road
Chorlton
Manchester M21 9QN
0161-881 1937

The Psychotherapy Centre
1 Wythburn Place
London W1H 5WL
0171-723 6173

Relate National
Herbert Gray College
Little Church St
Rugby CV21 3AP
01788 573241

Westminster Pastoral Foundations
23 Kensington Square
London W8 5HN
0171-937 6956

Women's Therapy Centre
6–9 Manor Gardens
London N7 6LA
0171-263 6200

AUDIO TRAINING EXERCISES

Deep relaxation training ● Assertiveness training

The authors have developed and produced a 1-hour audio-tape to complement this book:

SIDE ONE provides an effective and simple-to-use programme of experiential learning exercises in Deep Progressive Muscle Relaxation. The use of relaxation techniques is central to most of the self-help programmes and approaches of this book. Audio-taped instructions are one of the most efficient ways to learn relaxation skills.

SIDE TWO contains a format for understanding and developing self-assertive behaviours in a wide variety of situations. It includes practice exercises to provide an initial acquisition of skills.

This 'Home Therapy' audio-tape is available at £9·50 per single copy. It is also available in packs of 5 at £41·50 per pack. Both prices include postage and packing.

Please make your cheque/postal order payable to 'Home Therapy' and send it with this completed form to Winslow Press Ltd, Telford Road, Bicester, Oxon OX6 0TS, United Kingdom.

Please send ☐ Home Therapy audio-tapes at £9·50 each

Please send ☐ Home Therapy 5-tape packs at £41·50 each

NAME _____

ORGANIZATION _____

ADDRESS _____

_____

_____ POSTCODE _____

I enclose a cheque/postal order for £ _____ made payable to 'Home Therapy'.